CONTENTS

CHAPTER ONE

The Sentence

When you say something or write something, you want to be understood by other people. You want your words to make sense. When you put words together and they do not make sense, you have written (or spoken) nonsense, and other people will not understand you.

In this chapter, you shall study some of the basic rules for making sentences that people will understand.

What Is a Sentence?

Let's look first at three different groups of words:

EXAMPLES   around the corner on two wheels (Something must have been going too fast. What was it? A baby carriage? A road grader?)
broke in the middle (What broke?)
the fierce, high winds (What did the winds do?)

If you said any of these groups of words, listeners might complain that they did not understand you, or might ask you what you meant. That is because none of these groups of words say anything by themselves. They leave the listeners dangling. They are not sentences. But look at these groups of words:

EXAMPLES   The ice cream truck skidded *around the corner on two wheels.*
The film *broke in the middle.*
The fierce, high winds bent the television antenna.

Anyone who heard (or read) these groups of words would know what they mean. They are complete in themselves. They are sentences.

A sentence is a group of words expressing a complete thought.

Note that when you write a sentence, you show where the sentence begins by using a capital letter. You show where it ends by using a punctuation mark—a period, a question mark, or an exclamation point.

EXAMPLES   The new factory manufactures tires.
Why did you leave the movie before it was over?
That motorcycle almost crashed!

EXERCISE A   Half of the groups of words that follow are sentences, but the beginning capital letters and the end punctuation have been left out. In the space at the left of each, write *S* if the group is a sentence and *NS* if it is not. (Add 10 points for each correct answer.)

...... 1. three business leaders organized a fund-raising drive

...... 2. she drove to Mexico City with her parents

...... 3. saying that custard was her favorite dessert

...... 4. the road made a hairpin turn

...... 5. before doing any of the extra-credit problems

...... 6. the cost of a new car when you trade it in every year

...... 7. stayed up watching television until after midnight

...... 8. a red light blinking on and off at the top of the tower

...... 9. we got lost on the new express highway

...... 10. he saw her in the baked goods section of the supermarket

EXERCISE B   Complete the following sentences by writing in each blank the word or words in parentheses that complete the thought. (Add 10 points for each correct sentence.)

1. Harriet and Lori .... karate lessons. (take, taking)

2. .... practice one hour every night. (And, They)

3. They must .... thirty push-ups at each practice. (do, doing)

4. .... will make their arms stronger. (If this, This)

5. .... work out in a gym called a *dojo*. (Since they, They both)

6. Each .... a white suit called a *gui*. (wears, wearing)

7. The instructor .... very patient. (is, being)

8. .... shows them the technique of the side kick many times. (Because he, He)

9. The instructor .... a black belt wrapped around his waist. (has, having)

10. .... that he is a master. (This means, Meaning)

2

Subject and Predicate

There are all sorts of sentences, some long and some short. All of them, however, have two necessary parts: a *subject* and a *predicate.*

The subject of a sentence is that part about which something is being said.

The predicate of a sentence is that part which says something about the subject.

EXAMPLE   Carmen moved here from Cuba.

The sentence is *about* Carmen. Carmen is the subject of the sentence. What is being said about Carmen? Carmen moved here from Cuba; *moved here from Cuba* is the predicate of the sentence.

In the following examples, the subject is separated from the predicate by a red line. The part of the sentence before the line is the *subject.* The part after the line is the *predicate.* As you read each sentence, ask yourself *what it is about* (the subject) and *what it says about the subject* (the predicate).

EXAMPLES   The truck | carried six brand-new cars straight off the boat from Europe.
The meadow in a clearing in the woods | was carpeted with daisies.

Notice that the subject of a sentence may be quite long and the predicate quite short—or the other way around. The important thing, of course, is not length at all, but the job the words do in each part of the sentence. In the first example, the words that tell what the sentence is about are *the truck,* which is therefore the *subject.* Every other word tells what the truck did, and belongs, therefore, to the *predicate.* The second example uses several words to say what the sentence is about. The *subject* is *The meadow in a clearing in the woods.* The four remaining words say something about this subject and are the *predicate* of the sentence.

EXERCISE A   Use a vertical line to separate the subject and the predicate in each of these sentences. (Add 5 points for each correct answer.)

A. Dad | bought a new car last week.

1. This new car is for his personal use.

2. He goes to work in it.

3. We kept our old car.

4. We have never had two cars before.

3

5. The old car is for the use of the whole family.

6. Dad's new car is a small one.

7. My sister and I call it "The Bug."

8. Both the new car and the old car are painted red.

9. Half of the cars on our block are painted red.

10. Most of the people in our neighborhood must like red especially.

11. Several families on our block have two cars.

12. Almost all of the second cars are small.

13. Many of these smaller cars are made in Europe.

14. The European manufacturers ship them to this country by boat.

15. The duty on imported cars is, of course, considerable.

16. Most American manufacturers have increased their production of smaller cars.

17. This has been done to keep up with consumer demand.

18. Cars with smaller engines use less gasoline than cars with larger engines.

19. Some owners of larger cars have traded them for smaller models.

20. Others prefer the roominess and comfort of the larger vehicles.

EXERCISE B In the following sentences, underline the subject once and the predicate twice. If you are not sure what the subject is, ask yourself what the sentence is about (the subject) and what is being said about it (the predicate). (Add 10 points for each correctly marked sentence.)

A. The frightened men ran across the street into the police station.

1. The late arrival of one passenger delayed the plane an hour.

2. Some people can speak both French and English.

3. The sore place on Harry's foot made him limp.

4. The famous movie actress concealed her disappointment.

5. Hardly any news photographers were present.

6. The lights in the houses along the shore came on one by one.

7. Every lighthouse has its own way of shining its light.

8. Two plain-clothes police detectives questioned him.

9. A goose with six goslings waddled down to the pond.

10. One got lost in the crowd at the department store.

Finding the Verb

The predicates you studied in Lesson 2 are called *complete predicates*. Most complete predicates contain a main word (or group of words) known as the *simple predicate*. The simple predicate is the most important part of the predicate—it is the *verb* of the sentence.

In many sentences, you can leave out all of the predicate except the verb and the sentence will still more or less make sense. This is because the verb is the most active and informative part of the predicate. It does the basic job of *telling something about the subject*.

The simple predicate, or verb, is the main word or group of words in the complete predicate.

EXAMPLE   The train | moved.

This is a complete sentence with a one-word predicate, *moved,* which is the verb. The predicate always contains a verb, but it often contains more.

EXAMPLE   The train | moved slowly across the viaduct to the other shore.

This time, *the train* is still the subject, and the predicate is all the rest of the sentence. But the verb is still *moved.* It gives the basic information about the train.

The verb in a sentence may be a group of words. The added words that make up a complete verb are called *helping verbs*—they help the main verb make a statement. In the following examples, the verbs are printed in red and the helping verbs are underlined.

EXAMPLES   The train | was blowing its whistle.

He | had heard the rumor before.

I | will have left before dawn.

The examples illustrate two of the commonest helping verbs. *Was* is a form of the helping verb *to be,* whose other forms are *am, is, are, were,* and *been. Had* is a form of the helping verb *to have,* which also includes *has.* These two important helping verbs are often combined with other helping verbs, such as *shall, will, can, could, should, would, will have, can be, should have been.*

EXERCISE A   Draw a line between the subject and the predicate. Then underline the verb, including any helping verbs. (Add 10 points for each correctly marked sentence.)

1. An artist from our town gave our school a picture.
2. She came into the school one day with the picture under her arm.
3. She asked one of the students the way to the principal's office.
4. The principal's office had been moved.
5. The flustered student forgot this.
6. He gave the artist the wrong directions.
7. The artist lost her way.
8. The principal was going past her old office just then.
9. She noticed a bewildered stranger.
10. The students should be delighted with the new picture.

EXERCISE B Underline the verbs in the paragraph below, including helping verbs. (Add 4 points for each correct answer.)

SMOKE EATERS

1 Just before noon, the siren in the fire station sounded. The fire
2 department had received news of a major forest fire. The fire had
3 been raging for two hours already. It was out of control. The people
4 at the scene called for help from our fire department. They knew
5 it would respond quickly. Our fire department always helps in such
6 emergencies. The fire fighters drove their trucks fifteen miles. At the
7 scene of the fire, they rushed their equipment into action. They put
8 their hoses into the river. With the pumps on the trucks, they sprayed
9 water on the fire. They coughed because of the smoke. Breathing
10 was becoming difficult. The smoke also made their eyes red. No one
11 would envy fire fighters at times like this. Everyone would respect
12 their bravery. Despite all their efforts, the fire raged for hours. The
13 heat forced the fire fighters back. Anyone would have felt discour-
14 aged. Slowly, however, a change came over the sky. Then suddenly
15 the rain was pouring down on them. Torrents of rain quickly damp-
16 ened the fire. Unless it is brought under control quickly, a forest fire
17 can be a great disaster.

Complete Subject and Simple Subject

Like the predicate of a sentence, the subject often consists of several words.

EXAMPLE   The dark-haired girl from Omaha swam across the lake.

What is the sentence about? The sentence is about the dark-haired girl from Omaha. *The dark-haired girl from Omaha* is called the *complete subject* of the sentence. Actually, the subject is neither about dark hair nor about Omaha. There is a main word in this, and in every complete subject. The main word in this complete subject is *girl*. The other words merely tell us *which particular* girl swam across the lake. *Girl* is called the *simple subject*.

The simple subject is the main word in the complete subject.

In this book, the *simple subject* will be referred to simply as the *subject.* You will have no trouble locating the subject of a sentence if you find the verb first. When you have found the verb, ask the question *who?* or *what?* before the verb. The answer will always be the subject of the sentence.

EXAMPLES   A nine-car passenger train was stolen.   (*What* was stolen? *Train* was stolen. *Train* is the subject.)

A visitor from outer space asked to see our leader.   (*Who* asked? *Visitor* asked. *Visitor* is the subject.)

Usually, a group of words must have a subject (and a verb) or it cannot be a sentence. The only important exception is the *imperative* sentence, which states a command or makes a request.

IMPERATIVES   Open the window! Wait your turn, please.

Imperative sentences do not have an expressed subject. The subject *you*—the person to whom we are speaking—is the *understood subject* of an imperative sentence.

EXERCISE A   Underline the complete subject once and the verb (including helping verbs) twice. Two of the sentences are imperatives, with no expressed subject to underline. (Add 10 points for each correctly marked sentence.)

A. The whole basketball team will stay for dinner.

1. Any well-behaved person would have known better.

2. A coin-operated phonograph is called a juke box.

3. I must have dropped our tickets for the movie.

7

4. Give them to your father right away.

5. George will have left for the movies already.

6. That bad-tempered ticket seller gave me the wrong change.

7. The first cars in the parade passed near us.

8. Suckling pig is one of Mother's favorite dishes.

9. We can sleep out in our tents tonight.

10. Please send the package to me by parcel post.

EXERCISE B Underline the complete subject, and then write the simple subject in the blank at the right. (Add 5 points for each correctly marked sentence.)

1. Seven bearded miners appeared without warning. . . . .

2. The excited townspeople watched them warily. . . . .

3. This isolated desert town never had seen such a sight. . . . .

4. No passing traveler had mentioned seeing them. . . . .

5. Nobody knew anything about the miners. . . . .

6. The exhausted strangers trudged down the street. . . . .

7. They went straight to the county clerk's office. . . . .

8. Nothing could stop the hungry, thirsty men. . . . .

9. Each miner filed a claim. . . . .

10. These new claims lay together on Bald Mountain. . . . .

11. Several curious townspeople questioned the miners. . . . .

12. The miners cautiously evaded their questions. . . . .

13. The exact location of their claims remained a secret. . . . .

14. The silent, secretive group stayed around town. . . . .

15. An ambitious young reporter tried to interview the miners. . . . .

16. The local newspaper wanted their story. . . . .

17. The editor of the paper promised the reporter a large bonus. . . . .

18. The miners agreed to remain silent. . . . .

19. None would talk to the reporter. . . . .

20. The disappointed reporter returned to the editor without the scoop. . . . .

Sentences with Compound Parts

Many sentences have subjects with more than one part or verbs with more than one part (or both). We call these more complicated sentence parts *compound subjects* and *compound verbs*.

When two (or more) connected verbs in a sentence have the same subject, the two (or more) of them together are called a compound verb.

EXAMPLES Joe intercepted a pass and ran for a touchdown.
Dorothy jumped the hurdle and ran to the finish line.
Olga played the piano and sang Swedish songs.

Subjects can be compound, too.

When two (or more) connected subjects in a sentence have the same verb, the two (or more) of them together are called a compound subject.

EXAMPLES Karate or judo can be used for self-defense.
Trains, planes, and cars account for most passenger traffic.

There are also sentences with both compound subjects and compound verbs.

EXAMPLES Rita and Herman hated skiing but loved skating.
Mom, Dad, and my brother flew to Chicago and drove back.

Notice that compound subjects are usually connected by *and* or *or.* Compound verbs may be connected by *and, or,* or *but.* These connecting words are called *conjunctions.* Commas are used to separate the parts of a compound verb or subject having more than two parts.

COMPOUND SUBJECT Willis, Ethel, and Paula have been nominated for class president.

COMPOUND VERB The rocket lifted from the pad, soared upward, and went out of sight.

EXERCISE A Draw two lines under the verbs in the following sentences. Then write *CV* (for compound verb) in the blank to the left of any sentence that contains a compound verb. (Add 10 points for each correctly marked sentence.)

CV A. The hurricane shook houses and blew the trees.

...... 1. The scene was one of devastation and destruction.

9

C.V. 2. One family <u>found</u> their automatic washer two blocks away
and <u>brought</u> it home in a wheelbarrow.

C.V. 3. Some parts <u>were</u> <u>missing</u> and never <u>were</u> <u>found</u>.

...... 4. Repairs to the washer <u>would</u> <u>cost</u> over one hundred and fifty
dollars.

C.V. 5. Instead, they <u>forgot</u> repairs and <u>bought</u> a new one.

...... 6. They <u>watched</u> expenses with great care.

C.V. 7. They <u>started</u> from scratch and <u>rebuilt</u> their house.

C.V. 8. A plumber <u>came</u> and <u>pumped</u> sand out of the cellar.

...... 9. Damage to the foundation and the wall <u>was</u> <u>repaired</u>.

C.V. 10. Upholstered furniture <u>was</u> <u>spoiled</u> and <u>could</u> not <u>be</u> <u>saved</u>.

EXERCISE B Draw one line under the subjects in the following sentences. Write *CS* (for compound subject) in the blank to the left of any sentence that contains a compound subject. (Add 10 points for each correctly marked sentence.)

CS A. A <u>dog</u> and a <u>girl</u> with a leash got out of the car.

...... 1. Tourists and sightseers visit the skyscraper.

...... 2. The overfilled pitcher promptly spilled.

...... 3. The lights on the neon sign flashed brightly.

...... 4. The headlights of the oncoming cars blinded them.

...... 5. Tables and chairs were turned topsy-turvy.

...... 6. Jagged rocks and pieces of dirt fell on the roof.

...... 7. A clown and a chimpanzee rode at the head of the parade.

...... 8. The wallpaper and the gold paint were peeling off.

...... 9. Two hawks soared above the valley on outspread wings.

...... 10. A fire fighter leaned out the window and dropped a small dog
into the net.

Simple and Compound Sentences

A *simple sentence* has only one subject and only one verb, although both may be compound. All of the sentences you have studied so far have been simple sentences.

A *compound sentence,* on the other hand, has two (or more) subjects and each subject has its own verb. It is really two (or more) simple sentences joined together, usually by a conjunction.

A compound sentence consists of two or more simple sentences usually joined by a connecting word.

SIMPLE SENTENCES   Roxanne caught a three-pound trout. We cooked it over an open fire.

COMPOUND SENTENCE   Roxanne caught a three-pound trout, and we cooked it over an open fire.

Notice the conjunction *and* which connects the two parts of the compound sentence. The conjunctions *but, or,* and *nor* may also be used to join the parts of a compound sentence. A comma is placed before the conjunction.

The big difference between a simple sentence and a compound sentence is not that one is long and the other short. A simple sentence may be quite long. A compound sentence may be quite short. But a compound sentence can always be broken up into its parts and the parts will still be sentences—they will make sense by themselves.

EXAMPLES   Frances Willard and Mary Lyon taught school and founded seminaries for girls in the nineteenth century. (simple sentence with compound subject—*Frances Willard* and *Mary Lyon*—and compound verb—*taught* and *founded*)

Fish swim, but birds fly. (compound sentence: *Fish swim* and *birds fly* make sense by themselves and can be written as two separate simple sentences)

EXERCISE A   Underline each subject once and each verb twice. Circle *C* if the sentence is compound, or *S* if the sentence is simple. Remember that a simple sentence may have compound parts. (Add 10 points for each correctly marked sentence.)

C Ⓢ   1. Leonardo da Vinci and Columbus were contemporaries.

Ⓒ S   2. Both lived during the Renaissance, and both had a strong desire for knowledge.

C (S) 3. The Renaissance began at the end of the fourteenth century and lasted for about two hundred years.

(C) S 4. Columbus was an Italian navigator, but he worked in the service of Spain.

(C) S 5. Columbus read every available book on geography and travel, and he dreamed of a new route to the Orient.

(C) S 6. At one time Leonardo studied some maps, and later Columbus used those same maps on his voyage to America.

(C) S 7. Columbus found a new world, but he failed to reach the Orient.

(C) S 8. Leonardo was one of the most famous men of his time, but he never gave up his studies.

C (S) 9. Leonardo was a gifted artist, inventor, and architect.

(C) S 10. Both men considered themselves failures, but they left a tremendous mark on history.

EXERCISE B Combine each of the following pairs of simple sentences into one compound sentence. Put a comma in place of the first period and cross out the capital letter with which the second sentence begins. Insert the conjunction *and, but,* or *or,* depending on which makes the best sense. Notice the example. (Add 10 points for each correctly marked sentence.)

A. The pond was frozen, ⟨and⟩ We decided to go ice-skating.

1. Pat lives next door to me, ⟨but⟩ We never walk to school together.

2. Our house is painted yellow, ⟨and⟩ The shutters are painted white.

3. Ann Boston is the class president, ⟨and⟩ She is also the yearbook editor.

4. You can rake the lawn, ⟨or⟩ You can go to a movie. (either one—use *or*)

5. Pearl must be sick, ⟨or⟩ She would be in class today. (Which conjunction makes sense here?)

6. The oak was struck by lightning, ⟨but⟩ It is still alive.

7. Rosalie worked in a lumberyard, ⟨and⟩ Mario delivered newspapers.

8. I washed the car on Saturday, ⟨and⟩ Today I am going on a picnic.

9. Paul studied for three hours, ⟨and⟩ He forgot to memorize the poetry.

10. Bart promised to pay me back, ⟨but⟩ He never did.

12

Chapter Review

EXERCISE A Some of the following are sentences and some are not. Circle *S* before the items that are sentences and *NS* before the items that are not sentences. (Add 20 points for each correct answer.)

(S) NS 1. You can often get tacos from pushcart vendors.

(S) NS 2. We bought some on our trip to New York.

S (NS) 3. Standing around Central Park.

S (NS) 4. People selling tacos and tamales from umbrella stands.

(S) NS 5. A tamale is very hot.

EXERCISE B Some of the following sentences are simple, and some are compound. In each sentence, underline the *subject* (or *subjects*) once and the *verb* (or *verbs*) twice, including helpers. Watch out for compound subjects and verbs. (Add 5 points for each correct sentence.)

A. During the Dark Ages, life and property were unsafe.

1. In A.D. 374 the Huns crossed the Volga River and entered Europe.

2. They were a nomadic and warlike tribe from Asia.

3. In 451 Attila and the Huns swept across Europe.

4. Attila spared the city of Rome, and his army withdrew from Italy.

5. In 476 the Germans fought and defeated the Roman army.

6. The Dark Ages began with the fall of Rome and lasted about five hundred years.

7. Gradually some barbarians settled down and lived more peacefully with the Romans, and the Romans taught them civilized customs.

8. The Romans called all foreigners barbarians, but today the word means "uncivilized" or "savage."

9. Poor Roman farmers would sell their lands and work for wealthy landowners.

10. In time they became serfs, and their descendants forgot past glories.

11. Serfs were bound to the land and were sold with it.

12. The serfs would work much of the time in the noble's castle and would farm the noble's lands.

13. Cities often had walls around them, and large churches were built inside the walls.

14. Artisans wove intricate tapestries, and these hung on the city walls.

15. Some of these tapestries have survived and are hanging in museums.

16. Small wars and invasions were common.

17. The markets and fairs spread new ideas.

18. Famines and plagues were frequent, and thousands of people would die.

19. Later in the Middle Ages, strong rulers gathered armies and stopped the frequent wars between feudal lords.

20. Nations grew up with kings or queens as rulers, and the lords became their vassals.

EXERCISE C   Write the appropriate letter (*a, b, c,* etc.) in front of each sentence to explain what kind of sentence it is according to the following code: (Add 10 points for each correct answer.)

a—simple sentence with one subject and one verb;
b—simple sentence with compound subject;
c—simple sentence with compound verb;
d—simple sentence with compound subject and compound verb;
e—compound sentence.

. . . . 1. Many famous speakers and writers blunder in their speech and make errors in their writing.

. . . . 2. W. A. Spooner was an English clergyman.

. . . . 3. He made many blunders during his sermons, and these blunders are called *spoonerisms.*

. . . . 4. Spooner would switch the first consonants of two words and would accidentally form two new words.

. . . . 5. He said the *bl*ushing *cr*ow for the *cr*ushing *bl*ow and a half-warmed *f*ish for a half-*f*ormed *w*ish.

. . . . 6. Spooner said *ki*nquering *co*ngs, but we study *co*nquering *ki*ngs.

. . . . 7. Sometimes blunders and boners are humorous.

. . . . 8. Often comedians and humorists make a blunder and pull a boner.

. . . . 9. The Latin term for a slip of the tongue is a *lapsus linguae.*

. . . . 10. You and I could call a slip of the pen a *lapsus calami.*

14

Building Vocabulary: Words and Experience

Language provides a number of ways of discovering the meanings of words and of adding them to your vocabulary. In these vocabulary lessons, you will learn to use these methods systematically. As a start, let's consider what is meant by *context* and how it can help.

The context, or situation, in which a word is used shows what it means in that instance.

The first time you go bowling, you know the words *strike* and *spare* already, but you probably do not know what they mean in bowling. You learn in a variety of ways: from seeing someone make a strike or a spare, from hearing someone explain how it is done, and from observing how it affects the score.

These experiences teach you the meanings of the special words that go with bowling. When you use the words again, you will remember the *situations* in which you first learned them. In the same way, you learned the baseball meaning of *strike* and perhaps its meaning in fishing and in labor-management relations. Each of these situations adds something to the meaning that the word *strike* has for you. The situation in which a word is used—everything that you and others do and say—is called its *context*.

Study the meanings and examples given for the words below. Try to think of contexts in which you might use each word. Then try yourself out in the exercise. The two charts (on page 252 and inside the back cover) contain the symbols for the pronunciations given after each vocabulary word.

aristocrat /ə rís tə krat/, *n.* A member of a class that enjoys certain privileges and responsibilities by birth; a leader in society because of wealth, talent, or intelligence: *Many of the leaders of the American Revolution were aristocrats.*—**aristocracy** /ár is tók rə sē/, *n.*

balmy /bá mē/, *adj.* Mild, soft, soothing: *Everyone enjoyed the balmy spring weather.*

blemish /blém ish/, *n.* Any mark of imperfection; a surface flaw: *This tomato is perfect, without a blemish. A spiteful tongue is a blemish on one's character.*

farce /fars/, *n.* A short, broadly comic play; a ridiculous affair or action, an absurd failure: *Slapstick comedy is the kind of play called farce. The baseball game was a farce—we lost 20 to nothing.*

gaudy /gáu dē/, *adj.* Brightly colored and showy but in bad taste: *The man's hand-painted tie, which was orange and green, was rather gaudy.*

mimic /mím ik/, *v.* To imitate closely, usually with a comic effect: *Small children often mimic their parents. Everyone mimicked Ellen's British accent.*

protrude /prō trū́d/, *v.* To stick out from the surface of something: *Only a little of an iceberg protrudes above the water.*

ravenous /ráv ən əs/, *adj.* Frantically hungry: *After two days without food, the dog was ravenous.*

replica /rép lə kə/, *n.* An exact copy: *That painting in our living room is not an original but a replica of it.*

submerge /səb múrj/, *v.* To go or to put under water: *The alligator submerged in the river until only its head was showing.*

15

EXERCISE   Each of the numbered items below describes a situation, or context, in which you could use one of the words defined in this lesson. Decide which of the ten words would be most appropriate in each situation and write the word in the space provided. (Add 10 points for each correct answer.)

1. *Situation:*   A submarine dives to escape detection by the enemy.

   Word: . . . .

2. *Situation:*   A house is painted in red and yellow stripes.

   Word: . . . .

3. *Situation:*   At Independence Hall in Philadelphia, where the Declaration of Independence was signed, you can buy a copy that looks exactly like the original document.

   Word: . . . .

4. *Situation:*   It is a beautiful spring day, warm and pleasant, neither too hot nor too cold.

   Word: . . . .

5. *Situation:*   Your father notices a nail sticking up from a board on the front porch and asks you to hammer it back in.

   Word: . . . .

6. *Situation:*   The head of the British government is often a wealthy person whose family has been important in public life for generations.

   Word: . . . .

7. *Situation:*   You laugh uproariously at an old movie on television in which two men chase each other around a roller-skating rink.

   Word: . . . .

8. *Situation:*   Your mother is nailing a toolshed together, and your little sister gets her toy hammer and starts hammering too.

   Word: . . . .

9. *Situation:*   After an all-day hike, the children come back to the camp for dinner, quickly gulp down all the food at their table, and immediately ask for seconds.

   Word: . . . .

10. *Situation:*   You have been helping your parents paint the living room, and after finishing, you discover a patch that you forgot, where the original color shows through.

   Word: . . . .

Before you begin this first spelling lesson, read the section "A Note on Spelling," on page 251, and become familiar with the two charts that follow it.

These charts will be referred to in many of the spelling lessons in this book. You should find them useful in learning to spell the *majority* of English words. Remember: When a letter appears between a pair of slanted lines, it is the *sound* that is being referred to; a letter alone refers to that *letter* itself.

Spelling: Do you add s or es?

Why does English add *s* to some words and *es* to others when forming the plural of a noun or changing the form of a verb? Why can't our language just add *s*? As you examine the words below, notice which ones add just *s*, and which add *es*.

1	*2*
chair—chairs	glass—glasses
brag—brags	furnish—furnishes
youth—youths	witch—witches
succeed—succeeds	tax—taxes
gallop—gallops	buzz—buzzes

Why do you suppose the words in list *1* need add only *s*, and yet those in list *2* require *es*? Pronounce the words in the left-hand column of list *2*, paying special attention to the final sound of each word. Notice that the endings all sound like some form of a hiss. Such hissing sounds are known as *sibilants*. The final sounds in these words can be found in the chart "Consonant Sounds and Their Common Spellings" on page 252 listed under /s/, /sh/, /ch/, and /z/. (The letter *x* is not listed on the chart because it usually represents two separate sounds: /k/ and /s/. Nevertheless, words that end in *x* have a final *sound* of /s/.)

Now, attempt to add still another sibilant, /s/, to these words that already end in a sibilant. Try saying *furnishs, taxs,* etc. The words become unpronounceable. To say these words and others with a sibilant at the end, you must add another *syllable, es,* to the original word.

Add es to form the plural of a noun or change the form of a verb if the word ends in s, sh, ch, x, or z.

EXERCISE A   Pronounce the words below. Decide whether you must add *s* or *es* to each to form the plural of the noun or change the verb.

Then write the words in the blanks, adding *s* or *es*. (Add 10 points for each correct answer.)

1. villain . . . .   6. waltz . . . .
2. progress . . . .   7. approach . . . .
3. highway . . . .   8. brick . . . .
4. panic . . . .   9. relax . . . .
5. accomplish . . . .   10. gas . . . .

EXERCISE B Write *s* or *es* at the end of each italicized word in the sentences below. Again, use the "sound" test before deciding. (Add 10 points for each correct answer.)

1. Many college *campus* . . . . . . are less crowded these days.
2. Our dog *cough* . . . . . . whenever it smells dust.
3. Pam's little brother *follow* . . . . . . her everywhere.
4. Soda water *fizz* . . . . . . when you open the bottle.
5. There are two *church* . . . . . . at the north end of town.
6. Please put those books into two separate *box* . . . .
7. In the distance, we saw two bright *flash* . . . . . . of light.
8. Most large cities have many *problem* . . . . . . to solve.
9. Jan broke her leg and must use *crutch* . . . . . . for a while.
10. Laura certainly *express* . . . . . . herself clearly.

EXERCISE C Complete each italicized word in the paragraph below by writing *s* or *es* in the blank. Pronounce the words before deciding on the endings. (Add 10 points for each correct answer.)

1   The pelican *catch* . . . . . . fish with its pouch. The pouch is also used
2   to store fish while the bird *search* . . . . . . for more prey. The pelican
3   *pass* . . . . . . over the water. When it *sight* . . . . . . a fish, it *fix* . . . . . .
4   the point in its mind and *whizz* . . . . . . to the water. The *splash* . . . . . .
5   made by the pelican's body as it repeatedly *hit* . . . . . . the water can be
6   heard for almost half a mile. The pouch *stretch* . . . . . . to make room
7   for the fish and water. A greedy pelican often *fall* . . . . . . on its face
8   because of the weight of its pouch.

CHAPTER TWO

Words That Build Sentences

In ENGLISH WORKSHOP, words are the tools used to build sentences. There are many words in the WORKSHOP, but only a few *kinds* of words. Being familiar with these various kinds of words and knowing how they are used helps you to build strong sentences. This chapter is about six basic kinds of words. As a group, they are called the *parts of speech.*[1]

LESSON 10

Nouns

The subject of a sentence is usually the kind of word called a *noun*. When you write or talk, you are writing and talking about things, and nouns are the words that name these things.

A <u>noun</u> is a word used to name a person, place, thing, or idea.

In the following sentences, the words printed in red are all nouns. Notice which nouns name persons and which name places, things, or ideas.

EXAMPLES   **Willa Cather** wrote **stories** about the **Midwest**.
Alaska is the largest **state** in the **Union**.
This **table** needs another **coat** of **shellac**.
Clarity is a **quality** for which all good **writers** strive.

Here are some nouns of each of the four types:

PERSONS   Ann, Mr. Smedley, mother, children, painter, teacher
PLACES   Egypt, street, park, school, West Virginia, continent, home
THINGS   chair, clock, money, cobra, bicycle, dog, car, robin
IDEAS   honesty, freedom, power, happiness, curiosity, wisdom

Usually there are several nouns in every sentence.

EXAMPLES   My **parents** heard **Martina Arroyo** sing *Aïda* at the **Metropolitan Opera House**.
Some **drugstores** sell **appliances** and **stationery** as well as **medicine**.
Some **people** value **power** above **freedom**.
A **plane** flying from **Boston** to **Seattle** crosses the **continent**.

[1]Two other parts of speech, the *conjunction* and the *interjection,* are not treated in this chapter.

EXERCISE A In each line, write three nouns that name persons, places, things, or ideas, as indicated by the italicized word at the beginning of the line. Notice the examples. (Add 5 points for each correct answer.)

Persons A. *child* . 1. . . . . 2. . . . . 3. . . . .

Places B. *city* . . . 4. . . . . 5. . . . . 6. . . . .

Things C. *umbrella* 7. . . . . 8. . . . . 9. . . . .

Ideas D. *truth* . 10. . . . . 11. . . . . 12. . . . .

Fill the blanks in the following sentences with nouns that make good sense. Do not use any noun twice.

13. My . . . . is painted red and green.

14. Marion likes . . . . better than . . . .

15. Geoffrey stood on a . . . . to hang the . . . .

16. . . . . and . . . . are much bigger than . . . .

17. . . . . and . . . . are both in South America.

18. We used the . . . . while the . . . . was broken.

19. Kay bought a silver . . . . instead of a . . . .

20. She made . . . . with her new . . . .

EXERCISE B Underline all the nouns in the following sentences. The words *we, us,* and *you* are *not* nouns. (Add 4 points for each correct answer.)

A. For weeks my family had planned a trip.

1. One day we got into the car and drove to a lake.

2. Because the road was uncrowded, the drive took only thirty minutes.

3. The water at the lake was just the right temperature.

4. We dived in and had a good time for about an hour.

5. The swimming place has a pier and a raft with a diving board.

6. You can imagine our disappointment when clouds blew up.

7. There was a storm threatening.

8. The first drops of rain told us we had to leave.

9. Before we got to the car, the rain was coming down in torrents.

10. That storm certainly ruined our outing.

Pronouns

A pronoun is a word used in place of a noun.

All of these words are pronouns:

COMMON PRONOUNS

I, me, my,* mine	we, us, our,* ours	anybody	one
you, your,* yours	they, them, their,* theirs	both	several
he, him, his*	myself	either	someone
she, her,* hers	ourselves	nobody	others
it, its*		none	

We can think of pronouns as noun substitutes. We use them in certain situations to make our meaning clear. Compare these two conversations.

WITHOUT PRONOUNS | Al and Sue were talking. "*Al* thought *Sue* would take that job," Al remarked.
"How did *Al* know that *Sue* had been offered a job?" Sue asked.
"*Al* was there when *Sue's* name came up," Al said.

WITH PRONOUNS | Al and Sue were talking. "I thought **you** would take that job," Al remarked.
"How did **you** know that I had been offered a job?" Sue asked.
"I was there when **your** name came up," Al said.

Notice how useful pronouns can be. In the first sentence, *I* replaces *Al* and *you* replaces *Sue;* in the second sentence, *you* replaces *Al* and *I* replaces *Sue;* and in the third, *I* replaces *Al* and *your* replaces *Sue's.*

EXERCISE A   Underline the pronouns. Notice the first line, which has been done for you. (Add 2 points for each correct answer.)

1   Mother saw Dawn and me at the door and asked us where we were

2   going. I had on my hiking boots and Dawn was carrying a knapsack

3   on her back. "We are going on a hike," I told her. "Our science

4   teacher is going to show us how to build a tepee."

5   "It sounds like an interesting project," she said. "Be sure to stay

6   near the group. I don't want either of you getting lost."

7   We told her we would be careful.

8   Dawn and I and Mrs. Rogers headed for Bailey's Woods. When we

9   got there, we found a whole troop of Scouts camping out.

*The starred words are called pronouns in this book but are sometimes treated as adjectives. Use the term your teacher prefers.

21

10   "We can't do much as long as they are here," I said.

11   "We can ask how long they will be here," Dawn suggested.

12   "Too long," I thought to myself.

13   We decided the scoutmaster would be able to tell us, but none
14   of the Scouts could tell us where he was. They were by themselves.
15   Several suggested that he must have gone for water. Others thought
16   he might be searching for a good trail. One believed he was foraging
17   for berries.

18   Then someone said that the scoutmaster was coming back. We saw
19   him bringing a large pail of water. They all filled their canteens from
20   it. As soon as their canteens were filled, they were ready to go. The
21   whole troop picked up their packs and hiked off. At last we had the
22   woods entirely to ourselves.

EXERCISE B Cross out each noun in italics and write a suitable pronoun
above it. Sometimes one pronoun will substitute for two or more words
(*they* for *Ginny and Percy*). (Add 5 points for each correct answer.)

1   Ginny Patterson is the smartest person in our class. ~~Ginny~~ *She* plans to
2   be a physicist. *Ginny* is the only member of the class who knows what
3   *the member* wants to be. The rest of *the members* haven't decided yet.
4   Ginny is already doing algebra. *Ginny* gets special tutoring from other
5   teachers. Everyone in *Ginny's* family is remarkable. *Ginny's* older
6   brother is a champion wrestler and halfback on the high school
7   football team. *Ginny's older brother's* name is Percy, but nobody calls
8   *Percy* that, because *Percy* doesn't like it. Everyone calls *Percy*
9   "Perce." *Ginny and Percy's* mother is a famous singer. *Ginny and*
10   *Percy's mother* was performing when *the mother* met *Ginny and*
11   *Percy's* father. *Ginny and Percy's* father is the state champion chess
12   player. *The father* is teaching Ginny how to play chess. Perce already
13   knows. Perce and Ginny play each other almost every day. *Chess*
14   is different from any other game, *Perce and Ginny* say. *Perce and*
15   *Ginny* also know how to play bridge, but *Perce and Ginny* prefer
16   chess.

Adjectives

An underline{adjective} is a word used to modify a noun or pronoun.

Modify means *to limit.* An adjective modifies, or limits, a noun or pronoun by making its meaning more specific. Instead of saying that Cicely lives in a house, we can say that she lives in a *brick* house, a *red* house, a *square* house, or even a *square red brick* house. The adjectives *square, red,* and *brick* make the meaning of *house* more specific. They set Cicely's house apart from all the other houses that do not have these qualities.

In the following sentences, the adjectives are printed in red and the words they modify are underlined.

EXAMPLES   The **new** car is in the driveway.   (modifies a noun)

Hand me **that big** book on the **top** shelf.   (modify nouns)

Hand me **that big** one.   (modify a pronoun)

Most adjectives answer the question *what kind? which one?* or *how many? (how much?).*

WHAT KIND?	WHICH ONE?	HOW MANY?
an **easy** answer	**that** apple	**no** questions
the **large** apartment	**those** peaches	**thirty-two** helicopters
canned new peas	the **third** line	a **dozen** astronauts
the **open** door	the **next** time	**many** friends

WHAT KIND?	WHICH ONE?	HOW MANY?
a **thin**, **round** cookie	the **oldest** show	**one** operation
a **furrowed** brow	the **highest** cloud	a **few** peanuts
heavy, **yellow** metal		
white plastic cement		
smiling eyes		

Notice that several of the expressions above include the words *a, an,* or *the.* Strictly speaking, these three common little words are also adjectives. They form a special category all their own and are called *articles.* Although you will find many articles in this book, you may disregard them in any exercises on identifying adjectives.

EXERCISE A   Underline the adjectives in the following sentences and draw an arrow from each adjective to the word it modifies. Do not underline the articles *a, an,* or *the.* (Add 10 points for each correctly marked sentence.)

A. Despite the terrible heat, everyone had a good time.

1. A hot, dry wind blew over the parched prairie town.

2. Unshaded thermometers rose to ninety-nine degrees.

3. The wilted citizens sought out the shadiest spots.

4. Huge, black thunderheads piled up on the horizon.

5. Panting dogs hid under the thickest bushes.

6. Crowded pools were filled with weary people seeking relief.

7. Some fortunate people with air conditioners stayed in their cool and comfortable homes.

8. The long, hot day drew to a close in a fiery sunset.

9. Thunder rolled from the storm clouds, and a delightful cool wind stirred the dusty elms along the main street of the town.

10. Soon a roaring summer downpour had brought an end to the heat wave.

EXERCISE B Underline each adjective. Write the letter *a*, *b*, or *c* above the adjective to show which question it answers about the word it modifies. (Add 4 points for each correct answer.)

Write *a* if the adjective answers the question *what kind?*
   b if the adjective answers the question *which one?*
   c if the adjective answers the question *how many?* (*how much?*)

FROM THE NEW WORLD

1 That remarkable sailor, Christopher Columbus, discovered rubber
2 during one of his first voyages to America. The rubber tree in those
3 days grew only in America. There were few ways to use rubber in
4 everyday living until the twentieth century. It did not even get an
5 ordinary name until a famous scientist discovered that it could rub
6 out pencil marks. The first practical use of rubber was as an eraser.
7 It was also used to make waterproof coats. These early rubber coats
8 melted in hot weather. An American inventor named Charles Good-
9 year discovered how to vulcanize rubber. Many kinds of rubber
10 clothing resulted. Vulcanized rubber is used for electrical insulation,
11 elastic bands, tires, and other items.

Verbs

A verb is a word that expresses action or otherwise helps to make a statement.

A verb is a necessary part of every sentence. It has the job of telling something about the subject. When a verb expresses action, the action may be physical (*jump*), or it may be mental (*believe*). Verbs that express physical or mental action are called *action verbs*.

ACTION VERBS   move, run, hit, jump, whirl, eat, talk, sleep, think, understand, speculate, wonder, prefer

Some verbs do not show action of *any* kind. They help to make a statement by linking the subject to a word in the predicate that describes or explains it. These verbs are called *linking verbs*. The linking verbs include various forms of *to be* (*am, is, are, was, were, been*).

Besides *to be,* other common linking verbs are *appear, become, feel, grow, look, taste, remain, seem, smell, sound.*

LINKING VERBS   Mrs. Polanski **is** the mayor of Toledo. (*is* links *Mrs. Polanski* and *mayor*)
I **became** sad at the sight. (*became* links *I* and *sad*)
Our school **looks** very old. (*looks* links *school* and *old*)

EXERCISE A   Underline the verbs in the following sentences. (Add 10 points for each correct answer.)

A. Toni <u>played</u> the bass guitar.

1. Amanda accompanied her on rhythm guitar.

2. They formed a rock group with two other friends.

3. Toad Hall Revival was the name of their band.

4. After several months of practice, the group sounded very professional.

5. Suddenly the vocalist moved to another city.

6. Janet took the place of the original singer.

7. Everyone in the group liked her style of singing.

8. Carla became the manager for the quartet.

9. They performed for an enthusiastic audience at the summer concert.

10. This marked the beginning of a successful career for the band.

Helping Verbs   Often, the exact meaning of a verb cannot be made clear without the help of a special kind of verb—a helping verb. In the following examples, the verbs are printed in red and the helping verbs are underlined.

EXAMPLES   Leroy's mother **has returned** from her trip.

The baby **should** not **be** hungry yet.

They **will** always **remain** friends.

Notice that words like *not* and *always* may come between a verb and its helper. Such words are modifiers and are *not* part of the verb.

Learn to recognize these common helping verbs:

HELPING VERBS   be (am, is, are—was, were—been)
          have (has, had)   will, would
          do (does, did)   may, might, can, could
          shall, should   must, ought (to)

EXERCISE B   Underline all the verbs in the following paragraph, including helping verbs. Circle the helping verbs as well as underlining them. Do *not* mark any modifiers that come between a verb and its helper. (Add 10 points for each correct answer.)

FRENCH BORDERS

1   Natural barriers ⟨have⟩ always separated France from neighboring
2   countries. On the north, west, and south, it is protected by the sea.
3   The Pyrenees Mountains form the rest of France's southern border
4   and divide France from Spain. The Alps rise in the southeast. Only
5   in the northeast has there ever been any danger from invaders. There,
6   France and Germany meet along the banks of the Rhine River.
7   Between France and Belgium, the land boundary crosses flat, open
8   country. As a result of its natural frontiers, France is larger than any
9   other European country except Russia.

Adverbs

Adjectives modify nouns and pronouns. Adverbs, another type of modifier, are even more useful.

An adverb is a word used to modify a verb, an adjective, or another adverb.

EXAMPLES   My father spoke **sharply** to me. (*Sharply* modifies the verb *spoke.*)

That pencil is **too** soft. (*Too* modifies the adjective *soft.*)

The game ended **rather** suddenly. (*Rather* modifies the adverb *suddenly.*)

We can sort out the various adverbs by the kinds of questions they answer about verbs, adjectives, and adverbs.

EXAMPLES   Arlene went **out.** (*Where* did Arlene go? She went *out.*)

They left **yesterday**. (*When* did they leave? They left *yesterday.*)

We **seldom** hurry. (*How often* do we hurry? We *seldom* hurry.)

Jim dresses **neatly**. (*How* does Jim dress? Jim dresses *neatly.*)

Most adverbs answer the question *where? when?* (or *how often?*) or *how?* The *how?* adverbs, most of which end in *–ly*, form by far the largest group. Here are some of the most frequently used adverbs of each kind.

WHERE?	away, around, back, elsewhere, here, nowhere, out, outdoors, somewhere, there, upstairs
WHEN? (HOW OFTEN?)	always, finally, later, monthly, never, now, once, often, promptly, seldom, sometimes, soon, then, today, twice, usually, weekly, yearly
HOW?	badly, boldly, brightly, coldly, coyly, happily, loudly, lovingly, patiently, quickly, sadly, shyly, slowly, somehow, thoroughly, well

A few adverbs are often used with adjectives and adverbs to answer the question *how much?*

EXAMPLES   He came home **very** soon. This is **more** important.

Constance is **unusually** intelligent.

HOW MUCH?	almost, more, much, only, quite, somewhat, too, very, especially, exceptionally, hardly, largely, nearly, particularly, really, scarcely, so, surprisingly

EXERCISE A   Circle the adverb in each of the sentences below, and draw an arrow from the adverb to the word it modifies. Watch out for adverbs which are separated from the words they modify, especially from verbs, as in the example. (Add 10 points for each correctly marked sentence.)

A. (Often) at our house we start do-it-yourself projects.

1. Yesterday I decided on a special project.

2. I carefully shortened the legs of an old dresser.

3. Next I placed a piece of plywood on top of the dresser.

4. Awkwardly, I nailed the plywood onto the top of the dresser.

5. I proudly showed my parents this new desk.

6. They then suggested a new coat of paint.

7. I looked around for a brush.

8. Dad had left a can of paint somewhere.

9. Finally we found the paint in the garage.

10. I painted the desk completely.

EXERCISE B   Fill in the blanks in the paragraph below with adverbs chosen from the adverb lists on page 27. Do not use the same adverb twice. (Add 5 points for each correct answer.)

1   I arrive . . . . at my piano teacher's house for my lesson.

2   My piano teacher . . . . delays my lesson by keeping another

3   pupil overtime. I . . . . sit for a long time waiting. I

4   . . . . sit in the waiting room. Sometimes I pace

5   . . . . around the room. I take the time to look . . . .

6   The student who comes before me plays . . . . I listen to

7   him . . . . I never play . . . ., but I do not always

8   play . . . . well, either. I . . . . enjoy waiting for my

9   lesson. I . . . . enjoy listening to other students. When they

10   . . . . finish, I am waiting . . . . My teacher

11   . . . . comes out to say hello. I return her greeting

12   . . . . The other student leaves . . . . I . . . .

13   like playing the piano except for practicing. But to play

14   . . . ., you have to practice . . . .

28

Kinds of Modifiers

You can turn almost any adjective into an adverb by adding *–ly.*

ADJECTIVE   complete   perfect   hopeful   violent   smooth   nice
ADVERB   complete**ly** perfect**ly** hopeful**ly** violent**ly** smooth**ly** nice**ly**

Some adjectives, however, already end in *–ly.*

ADJECTIVES   lovely, leisurely, pearly

It would be awkward to add another *ly* to adjectives like these in order to make them into adverbs. Therefore you do not make adverbs of them. Instead you usually use a group of words that give the same meaning as an adverb (in a *lovely* way, with a *pearly* appearance).

Some words may be used either as adjectives or as adverbs without any change. To make sure how a particular word is being used, ask yourself what it modifies. If the word modifies a noun or a pronoun, it is an *adjective.* If it modifies a verb, an adjective, or another adverb, it is an *adverb.*

EXAMPLES   The **early** bus leaves at six. (*Early* is an adjective modifying *bus.*)

She left **early** for school. (*Early* is an adverb modifying *left.*)

She jumped and landed **hard** (*Hard* is an adverb modifying *landed.*)

Jack likes **hard** candy. (*Hard* is an adjective modifying *candy.*)

Ellen is a **fast** typist. (*Fast* is an adjective modifying *typist.*)

She types **fast**. (*Fast* is an adverb modifying *types.*)

EXERCISE A   If the italicized word is an adjective, write *adj.* above it. If it is an adverb, write *adv.* When in doubt, find the word the adjective or adverb modifies. Remember that a word that modifies a noun or a pronoun is an adjective. A word that modifies a verb, an adjective, or an adverb is an adverb. (Add 5 points for each correct answer.)

1. The plane circled the field and *slowly* came in for a landing.

2. You should not drive too *fast,* but a *slow* driver can also be dangerous.

3. I arrived *late* for the meeting yesterday.

4. A *late* arrival is better than none.

5. Marjorie has been taking lessons on the cello *lately.*

6. The bell interrupted Arny's *leisurely* account of his trip.

7. Miss Remington certainly does work *hard.*

8. Pandas have *hardly* ever been born in captivity.

9. That was a *hard* test, but you should have passed it *somehow.*

10. I watched the *early* show, but I did not go to bed *early.*

11. The school bus *nearly* had an accident yesterday.

12. The driver backed up *carefully,* but a boy's bike was lying *near.*

13. Mr. Acoli *first* said that I could make up the test, but on *second* thought he changed his mind.

14. "You will go *far,* young man," Dr. Young *often* assured me.

EXERCISE B   Underline the adjectives in the following paragraph and circle the adverbs. (Do not underline *a, the,* or *an.*) If you are not sure about a word, find the word it modifies. Treat words like *my* and *his* as pronouns, not adjectives, unless your teacher directs you otherwise. (Add 2 points for each correct answer.)

A MODERN PLAYWRIGHT

1   Lorraine Hansberry is an especially interesting modern playwright.
2   Several years ago, New York drama critics proudly gave her their
3   highly respected award for the best American play of the new theater
4   season. She was then the youngest American playwright, the fifth
5   woman, and the first Black to achieve this honor. Her much cele-
6   brated play was *A Raisin in the Sun.*
7   Miss Hansberry deeply believed that all people have within them
8   the ability to somehow dramatically change the universe. She vividly
9   recognized the vast power of human potential once it has been forced
10   into action. Because she clearly saw the incredible beauty of every
11   person, she knew it is an enormous error to waste lives. She knew that
12   each person has some dream. If this dream dies, then a very impor-
13   tant part of a person's life surely dies. No dream can be allowed to
14   slowly shrivel up like "a raisin in the sun."
15   Recently *A Raisin in the Sun* was produced on Broadway as a
16   musical. Now called *Raisin,* the musical version of the popular play
17   incorporates the tribal music and dances of the African people.

Prepositions

When you write a sentence about two different things, you often want to show how one thing is related to the other. Take a cat and a tree, for instance. You could say that the cat was *in* the tree, *under* the tree, *near* the tree, *behind* the tree, *above* the tree, or use yet another word. *In, under, near, behind,* and *above* are all prepositions.

A **preposition** is a word used to show the relation of a noun or a pronoun to some other word in the sentence.

EXAMPLES   I will gladly lend that book **to** you.
The red house **on** the corner is ours.
The dog hid **underneath** the porch.
The flood damaged several buildings **near** the harbor.
He ran **after** the bus.

Here are some of the most commonly used prepositions:

COMMON PREPOSITIONS

about	before	during	of	to
above	behind	except	off	toward
across	below	for	on	under
after	beneath	from	outside	until
against	beside	in	over	up
along	between	inside	past	upon
among	beyond	into	since	with
around	by	like	through	within
at	down	near	throughout	without

EXERCISE A   In each blank insert a suitable preposition from the list above. Try to use as many different prepositions as possible. (Add 10 points for each correct answer.)

1. We rode our bicycles .... the bridge and .... the trail.

2. .... an hour, we had traveled ten miles.

3. .... this rate, we would reach town .... supper-time.

4. There was a good wind .... us.

5. Sharon rode .... some broken glass.

6. .... fifteen minutes, her front tire went flat.

7. Sharon repaired the tire . . . . a short time.

8. . . . . this time we rested.

Generally, a preposition does not stand alone in a sentence. Usually, it begins a group of words which ends with a noun or a pronoun.

A group of words which begins with a preposition and ends with a noun or a pronoun is called a prepositional phrase.

EXAMPLES   along the road   for you and them
near me   throughout lunch
below the bridge   between us and the airport

The noun or pronoun that follows a preposition is the *object* of the preposition. It may have one or more modifiers.

EXAMPLES   A man <u>on a horse</u> rode <u>across the field</u>.

A man <u>on a yellow horse</u> rode <u>across the wet rocky field</u>.

EXERCISE B   Underline the prepositional phrases in the paragraph below, including any modifiers. Circle each object of a preposition. (Add 5 points for each correct answer.)

TURTLES AND TRIBAL LAW

1   The turtle was an important animal <u>for many American Indians</u>. The
2   Iroquois believed that the world rested on a turtle's back. The turtle
3   is regarded by some tribes as very clever. In one story, through deceit,
4   the turtle beats the deer in a race. Some Pueblos perform a turtle
5   dance. They carry turtle-shell rattles at their knees, wear belts of bells,
6   and carry a gourd rattle in the right hand. During the turtle dance
7   of the Iowa tribe, the dancers imitate the turtle's movements.

Which Part of Speech?

Nouns, pronouns, verbs, adjectives, adverbs, and prepositions are the principal parts of speech. Every word in the English language can be classified as one or another part of speech. This idea is important and useful. When you analyze how a sentence is put together, you must usually decide what part of speech each word is.

Sometimes the form of a word gives a clue as to what part of speech it is. Some words have one form as nouns and change a little as verbs, adjectives, or adverbs.

NOUN	VERB	ADJECTIVE	ADVERB
strength	strengthen	strong	strongly
length	lengthen	lengthy	lengthily
beauty	beautify	beautiful	beautifully

A large number of words stay the same whether they are used as nouns, verbs, or adjectives. You cannot say what part of speech these words are unless you know how they are used.

EXAMPLES   A **calm** fell. (*Calm* names something. It is a *noun.*)
A **calm** scene lay ahead. (*Calm* modifies *scene* and is an *adjective.*)
Candy will **calm** them. (*Calm* tells an action and is a *verb.*)

Other words that may be used as nouns, adjectives, or verbs are: *square, telephone, storm, head, sail,* and *light.* (Try them in sentences of your own and see.)

A great many words can be used as *two* different parts of speech without any change of form. Notice the words printed in red in the following pairs of sentences.

EXAMPLES   The **air** is fresh. I **air** the blankets. (noun and verb)

Todd is coming **down** tomorrow. The monkey ran **down** the ladder. (adverb and preposition)

I bought a new **radio**. I like **radio** programs. (noun and adjective)

She went **outdoors**. I like the great **outdoors**. (adverb and noun)

He performs **daily**. It is a **daily** paper. (adverb and adjective)

EXERCISE A Write in the blank provided the part of speech of each italicized word. Be sure you know how the word is used before you decide. (Add 10 points for each correct answer.)

A. The voters may *ease* him out of office this fall. A. ... *verb* ...

B. She performs her duties with *ease*. B. ... *noun* ...

1. He could *tease* a smile out of a stone. 1. ....

2. Jerry is an awful *tease*. 2. ....

3. The strong *current* here is dangerous. 3. ....

4. He disliked the *current* fashion. 4. ....

5. The bird flew *over* the mountain. 5. ....

6. Are you coming *over* tonight? 6. ....

7. Can you *reverse* the order of the players? 7. ....

8. She put the car in *reverse*. 8. ....

9. We have to light the oven with a *match*. 9. ....

10. My new shoes *match* my coat very well. 10. ....

EXERCISE B In each sentence, write the part of speech of the word that would have to fill the blank for the sentence to make good sense. Do *not* write the word itself. (Add 10 points for each correct answer.)

A. We met *preposition* the show.

1. The eagle built its nest .... the top of the tree.

2. She .... her newspaper from cover to cover.

3. June twenty-first is the .... day of the year.

4. A python is a giant ....

5. Eighteen .... the legal voting age.

6. The telephone rings much too ....

7. The boxer hit him with a right .... the jaw.

8. .... told them that I would not go.

9. The three .... girls did a dance.

10. My cousin .... too much ice cream.

Chapter Review

EXERCISE A In the blanks in the following sentences, write in the word that best completes each statement. (Add 10 points for each correct answer.)

1. A noun names a person, place, thing, or . . . .

2. A word used in place of a noun is called a(n) . . . .

3. We can think of these words as noun . . . .

4. A word that modifies a noun or pronoun is called a(n) . . . .

5. A word that modifies a verb is called a(n) . . . .

6. Adjectives answer the questions what kind? which? and how . . . . ?

7. A(n) . . . . verb may be used with an action verb or a linking verb to make the meaning of the verb clear.

8. A linking verb is so called because it links the subject of a sentence to a word in the . . . .

9. A group of words that begins with a preposition and ends with a noun or pronoun is called a(n) . . . .

10. The noun or pronoun that follows a preposition is called the . . . . of the preposition.

EXERCISE B Over each word in italics write one of the following abbreviations to identify its part of speech: *n.* for a noun; *pron.* for a pronoun; *adj.* for an adjective; *v.* for a verb; *adv.* for an adverb; and *prep.* for a preposition. (Add 2 points for each correct answer.)

NEW YORK AND BACK

1   My *family* *made* a trip to New York *during* my parents' vacation.

2   *We* had *only* two days for sightseeing, so we *crowded* as much *into*

3   the *available* time as possible. *First,* all of us *took* a special *sightseeing*

4   bus *for* the high *points.* *This* bus *took* us to Wall Street, Radio City,

5   and Chinatown. *It* also went *through* Greenwich Village. The *next*

6   day was *clear,* and we *immediately* *decided* to go to the *top* of the

35

7   Empire State Building. The *view* was *excellent.* We *could* see as far

8   as *Connecticut.* The *official* guide told *us* the day was *unusually* clear.

9   *That* evening, we ate *at* a *French* restaurant. There *are* restaurants

10 *of almost* every *nationality* in New York. *Afterward,* we went to Radio

11 City Music Hall, where there was a *huge stage* show. On our way

12 home, we *went through* the Lincoln Tunnel. *Despite* our *hurry,* we

13 took *enough* time to see the *university in* Princeton, New Jersey. It

14 *has* a *particularly beautiful campus.* The *next* day we arrived *home*

15 *safely.*

EXERCISE C   Show the part of speech of the italicized words by writing the correct abbreviation above each word. Be sure you understand how the word is used in the sentence before making up your mind. (Add 5 points for each correct answer.)

1. People on the bus sometimes *step* on my toes.

2. The horse stumbled on the first *step* and refused to budge.

3. Willis ate a *leisurely* breakfast and sauntered off to school.

4. Do you *like* milk or lemon in your tea?

5. Silence fell in the room *like* a weight.

6. She has the *will* to succeed, but she *will* need more than that.

7. Work *fast* or you will never finish in time.

8. The driver completed a *fast* first lap and went on to win.

9. The child gave the conductor a *friendly* smile.

10. We all had a good *swim* at the lake.

11. Do you ever *swim* after Labor Day?

12. On the floor of the drugstore, Geraldo beheld a *ghastly* sight.

13. *Beside* the sundae lay a pool of malted milk.

14. He ate a banana split *besides.*

15. I often *down* a quart of milk when I am really thirsty.

16. Look *down* the mountain and tell me what you see.

17. The runner fell *down* at the finish of the race.

18. The pillows are filled with *down.*

19. The soldiers *long* for news from home.

Cumulative Review

A Draw a vertical line between the complete subject in each sentence and the predicate. Underline the verb in each sentence, including helping verbs. (Add 5 points for each correctly marked sentence.)

1. The world of dance attracts people from many backgrounds.
2. Maria Tallchief was born on the Osage reservation in Oklahoma.
3. She became the prima ballerina with the New York City Ballet Company.
4. Doris Humphrey spent her youth in Illinois.
5. She danced with Ted Shawn and Ruth St. Denis' company.
6. This dancer also created dances of her own.
7. One of the lead dancers with the American Ballet Theatre is Fernando Bujones, a native of Cuba.
8. The critics have praised him highly.
9. Any list of outstanding dancers must include Judith Jamison of Alvin Ailey's dance group.
10. Her skillful jazz movements thrill audiences.

In each of the following sentences, underline the complete subject and circle the simple subject.

11. Mikhail Baryshnikov is a classical ballet dancer.
12. He has danced in a work called *Pas de "Duke"* with Jamison.
13. The lovely ballet is set to the music of Duke Ellington, the jazz musician.
14. Another famous pair of dancers is Margot Fonteyn and Rudolf Nureyev.
15. Their fame is worldwide.
16. Their devoted audiences often bought tickets for their performances well in advance.
17. The number of admirers of ballet seems to be increasing greatly.
18. People are interested in both dances that tell stories and dances that have no real plot.
19. The great classical ballets such as *Swan Lake* and *Romeo and Juliet* are always popular.

20. A night at the ballet can be a memorable experience.

B Underline the simple subject once and the verb twice in each of the following sentences. Some sentences contain compound subjects, compound verbs, or both. Be sure to underline all parts of a compound subject or a compound verb. (Add 5 points for each correct answer.)

1   Real knowledge of the universe grew little from the time of
2   Aristotle, the great Greek philosopher, until the early years of the
3   seventeenth century. Copernicus had argued against Aristotle's
4   theories as early as 1530 but was too radical for the philosophers
5   and scientists of his time. Copernicus called the sun the center
6   of the universe. The invention of the telescope in 1608 began a
7   revolution in scientific thought. Galileo built his first telescope the
8   following year and soon made many improvements in it. He and
9   Kepler were working on similar problems at the same time and kept
10   in touch by letter. Galileo observed, with his improved telescope,
11   the mountains on the moon and the moon's rough and rocky surface.
12   People before his time accepted Aristotle's theory of a moon of
13   smooth crystal.

C In the space to the left of each sentence write one of the following code letters to show what kind of sentence it is. (Add 20 points for each correct answer.)

    a—simple sentence with one subject and one verb
    b—simple sentence with compound subject
    c—simple sentence with compound verb
    d—compound sentence

. . . .   1. The Chicago fire of 1871 was a terrible disaster, but some good results came from it.

. . . .   2. The rebuilders of the city had an enormous task and of necessity devised faster and more efficient construction methods.

. . . .   3. Chicago's new "balloon" houses have been standard for home construction ever since.

. . . .   4. The modern fireproof building, steel frame construction, and the first skyscrapers also originated in Chicago.

. . . .   5. Some of the tallest and most daringly original apartment buildings in the world have been built there in recent years.

Building Vocabulary: More About Context

In reading, the meaning of unfamiliar words can be determined by clues given by other words. This is known as determining the meaning of words by *context*. Context may mean the entire subject of a book or article, or only the surrounding words—the sentence or paragraph in which a word is used. The surrounding words are called the *verbal context*.

The verbal context determines in which of its possible meanings a word is used.

Most words in English have more than one standard meaning. The context shows which meaning a word *must* have for a sentence to make good sense.

EXAMPLES She played the **beam** of her flashlight on the roof of the attic. I could see that one of the **beams** was rotten.

In the first example you know that the *beam* is a *beam of light*. The second example makes good sense only if you take *beam* in a different sense—as the *beam of wood* that supports the roof of a house.

The verbal context may show a new or more precise meaning for a familiar word.

We build up our vocabularies from familiar words. When you read that "rust had *eaten* away the iron hinges of the door" you build on the general meaning of *eat* (*to consume*) the more precise meaning of what rust does to iron.

Study the two meanings given for each word below. Be ready to decide which meaning fits the context in the exercise that follows.

adhere /ad hír/, *v.* 1. To stick to, as glue does. 2. To agree with a person, a group, or an idea.

agitate /áj ə tāt/, *v.* 1. To make something move in an irregular way; to shake. 2. To stir up the mind or emotions.

concession /kən sésh ən/, *n.* 1. The act of giving in to someone, or the thing given. 2. A business operated on the premises of another business, by a lease.

exquisite /éks kwi zit/, *adj.* 1. Very beautiful, delicate, or refined. 2. Strong, intense, extreme.

frivolous /frív ə ləs/, *adj.* 1. Trivial, petty, unimportant. 2. Light-minded, gay, silly.

humane /hy-ū mǎn/, *adj.* 1. Kind, warm, sympathetic. 2. Of things or activities, tending to make human life better.

satire /sát īr/, *n.* 1. A kind of writing in which evil or foolishness is held up to scorn. 2. The use of wit and sarcasm to attack a person or action.

speculate /spék yə lāt/, *v.* 1. To think deeply about something, forming theories about it. 2. To invest money at considerable risk but with the hope of a good profit.

tolerate /tól ə rāt/, *v.* 1. To let something happen without trying to interfere. 2. To stand or put up with; to suffer or endure.

turbulent /tór byə lənt/, *adj.* 1. Stirred up; very excited or confused. 2. Causing discontent, disturbances.

EXERCISE The ten words defined in this lesson are used below in context. Only one of the two meanings given on page 39 applies in each context. Decide which meaning is appropriate and write the number of this meaning in the space to the left of each context. (Add 10 points for each correct answer.)

.... 1. Adhesive tape is so named because it *adheres* to things.

.... 2. The mechanism of a washing machine *agitates* the clothes in order to make them clean. A wind *agitates* the surface of a lake.

.... 3. Last summer, my sister ran the candy *concession* at the theater.

.... 4. The design of the ancient tapestry, which was worked out in delicate colors and in great detail, was *exquisite*.

.... 5. We all enjoyed the *frivolous* comedy we saw on television.

.... 6. A *humane* judge takes account of a criminal's background in passing sentence.

.... 7. The speaker spoke sarcastically of her opponents' program and made them uncomfortable with her biting *satire*.

.... 8. Until we have more facts, there is little point in *speculating* about life on other planets.

.... 9. After my illness, my eyes could not *tolerate* bright light.

.... 10. The canoe swung wildly this way and that and nearly capsized in the *turbulent* waters below the rapids.

REVIEW EXERCISE In the space to the left of each word, write the letter of the best meaning listed at the right. (Add 10 points for each correct answer.)

.... 1. blemish   a. a member of a privileged class

.... 2. mimic   b. to go under water

.... 3. gaudy   c. to stick out

.... 4. replica   d. to imitate

.... 5. balmy   e. a surface flaw

.... 6. protrude   f. frantically hungry

.... 7. submerge   g. showy

.... 8. ravenous   h. an exact copy

.... 9. aristocrat   i. mild

.... 10. farce   j. an absurd failure

Spelling: Choosing Between ie and ei

As you remember from your reading of "A Note on Spelling" (page 251), the English language has more sounds than it has letters in the alphabet to represent them. Furthermore, you saw in your examination of the consonant and vowel charts that the same sound can often be spelled in *more* than one way. These two facts about our language account for the difficulty almost all of us have in spelling words containing the vowel combinations of *ie* and *ei*.

The following words all have *ie* or *ei* in them: *fiend, friend, mischief, height, foreign,* and *rein.* They look and sound so different that you may think them impossible to group or spell correctly. Fortunately, there is a simple rhyme which can help you with the *ie–ei* problem:

RHYME	EXAMPLES		
Use *i* before *e*,	brief	believe	friend
Except after *c*,	receive	ceiling	perceive
Or when sounded like /ā/,	freight	weight	veil
As in *neighbor* or *weigh*.			

EXERCISE A   Using the information you have learned, write *ei* or *ie* in the blanks in each word in the sentences below. Say the rhyme to yourself to help you decide which order of letters is correct. (Add 10 points for each correct answer.)

1. There are . . . . . .ght (one more than seven) club members present.

2. He is so conc. . . .ted about his part in the play that he won't talk to anyone.

3. Laura is Uncle Ted's favorite n. . . . . .ce.

4. In a monarchy, the king or queen r. . . . . .gns supreme.

5. Jeffrey heaved a sigh of rel. . . . . .f at his lucky escape.

6. When did you rec. . . . . .ve that strange message?

7. How much w. . . . . .ght did you gain?

8. We will try to keep the meeting br. . . . . .f.

9. Lynn conc. . . . . .ved of the perfect football tactic.

10. Karen and Marcia promised that they would always tell each other the truth and never practice dec. . . . . .t.

Certain words do not fit into the groups that you have been studying. Here are five of these exceptions:

neither   either   seize   weird   leisure

In each word above *ei* is used despite the fact that it is neither "after *c*" nor "sounded like /ā/." Therefore, you must simply memorize the spelling of these five words.

Other exceptions are:

height   foreign

Can you explain why these two words are also exceptions?

EXERCISE B Correctly fill in the blank in each of the following words with *ei* or *ie*. (Add 5 points for each correct answer.)

1. n......ghborly
2. rec......pt
3. f......ld
4. h......ghten
5. v......n
6. w......rdly
7. for......gner
8. shr......k
9. misch......f
10. ......ghteen

11. l......surely
12. gr......ve
13. sh......ld
14. p......ce
15. sl......gh
16. th......f
17. pr......st
18. fr......ndly
19. s......zure
20. rel......ved

EXERCISE C Use any ten words from Exercise B above in sentences of your own. Write your answers on a separate piece of paper. Underscore the *ei* and *ie* words. (Add 10 points for each correctly spelled *ei* or *ie* word.)

REVIEW EXERCISE Pronounce each word below. Decide whether you must add *s* or *es* to each to form the plural of the noun or to change the verb. Then write the *s* or *es* form of the word in the blank. (Add 10 points for each correct answer.)

1. glass ....
2. witch ....
3. tax ....
4. buzz.....................
5. gas ....

6. relax ....
7. church ....
8. approach ....
9. waltz ....
10. furnish ....

CHAPTER THREE

The Sentence Base

The flexibility of the English language makes it possible to write sentences of great length. But even the longest and most complicated sentence is built up on a straightforward and easily grasped framework called the *sentence base*. There are fundamentally only a few ways in which sentences can be put together. Once you recognize the basic kinds of English sentences, you can fit any sentence into one of these patterns, and you can build up sentences of your own on one of them. A firm grasp of the sentence base is one of the basic tools in ENGLISH WORKSHOP for saying *exactly what you mean* in writing.

LESSON 22

The Sentence: A Framework for Ideas

A sentence may have a two-part base consisting of the simple subject and the verb.

EXAMPLES   The parachute jumper | sank gently down.

My father and Uncle Jim | went to Duluth and stayed for a week.

Both of the sentences above are built up on a two-part base consisting of the subject and the verb. The parts of the sentence base may be compound, as in the second example, which has a compound subject and a compound verb. All of a sentence except the sentence base may be omitted, and the sentence will still be complete—it will make complete sense.

EXAMPLES   The jumper | sank.

Father and Uncle Jim | went and stayed.

The following subject-verb groups are *not* complete by themselves. In both of these examples something is missing.

EXAMPLES   The batter hit (*What* did the batter hit?)
That man is (*Who* or *what* is that man?)

The missing part in both of these examples is called the *complement* because it is necessary to *complete* the meaning of the verb.

Many sentences have a three-part base consisting of the simple subject, the verb, and the complement.

43

EXAMPLES The batter | hit | a home run.   That man | is | a liar.

Like the subject and the verb of a sentence, the complement may be compound—made up of two or more parts.

EXAMPLE Mary Ellen | wore | her new pantsuit and turtleneck sweater.

Subjects and complements are never found in a prepositional phrase.

EXAMPLE The stories in this book held my interest.

The subject is *stories,* not *book,* which is in the prepositional phrase *in this book.*

EXAMPLE I bought one of her tennis rackets.

The complement is *one,* not *rackets,* which is in the prepositional phrase *of her tennis rackets.*

EXERCISE In the following paragraph, underline the simple subject of each sentence once and the verb twice. Circle the complement whenever there is one. Then, in the space at the end of the sentence, write *2* if the sentence has a two-part base and *3* if the sentence has a three-part base. (Add 5 points for each correctly marked sentence.)

1 The newspaper in our town held a frisbee contest. (3) The judges
2 established a set of rules. ( ) The grand prize was a trip to San
3 Francisco. ( ) The judges created three contest divisions. ( ) One
4 division involved competition between two players. ( ) The second
5 division tested distance. ( ) The winner threw the frisbee further than
6 any other contestant. ( ) The last division involved a test of accuracy.
7 ( ) Frisbees were hurled through a hoop. ( ) Salvatore and Annette
8 both entered. ( ) Annette practiced steadily for a week. ( ) This was
9 her first contest. ( ) Sometimes she and Salvatore practiced to-
10 gether. ( ) Salvatore had been a contestant in two other contests.
11 ( ) The day of the contest arrived. ( ) Both Salvatore and Annette
12 were nervous. ( ) Salvatore entered the third division. ( ) He
13 did not win. ( ) Annette joined the first division competition. ( )
14 She was defeated by a more experienced contestant. ( ) Annette
15 and Salvatore will compete again next year. ( )

Action Verbs and Linking Verbs

A verb is a word that (1) *expresses action* or otherwise (2) *helps to make a statement*. These two different jobs are done by two different kinds of verbs. These two different kinds of verbs are called *action verbs* and *linking verbs*.

1. An action verb may occur in a two-part sentence base or in a three-part sentence base.

TWO-PART BASE The big tiger cat | suddenly leaped.
Marion | stood absolutely still.

THREE-PART BASE The ferocious bulldog | chased | the tiger cat.
Ben | remembered | his last birthday.
Caroline | always loved | horseback riding.

Notice that the action expressed by an action verb may be either physical (*leaped, stood, chased*) or mental (*remembered, loved*).

2. A linking verb usually occurs in a three-part sentence base.

The most common of all linking verbs is the verb *to be*. You should know and recognize its basic forms: *am, is, are, was, were, been*. Other common linking verbs are *appear, become, feel, grow, look, remain, seem, smell, sound,* and *taste*. Linking verbs are usually found in sentences with three-part bases because their job is to link the subject with a word in the predicate that describes or explains it (the complement).

THREE-PART BASE That cat | is | a fast runner.
The car's two front tires | were | flat.
Rhoda | seems | quite happy.

EXERCISE A The verbs in the sentences below are italicized. Circle the *A* to the left of the sentence if the verb is an *action verb;* circle the *L* if it is a *linking verb*. (Add 10 points for each correct answer.)

A L   1. Our school *produced* a play last year.

A L   2. Students *wrote* the entire play.

A L   3. All the actors *were* students also.

45

A L   4. One teacher *became* the director of the play.

A L   5. The play *portrayed* the history of our state.

A L   6. All the students in the play *were* outstanding in English.

A L   7. The play *went* smoothly, in spite of a few setbacks.

A L   8. The audience *enjoyed* it immensely.

A L   9. They *applauded* with enthusiasm at the end.

A L 10. Our teacher *seemed* equally well satisfied with us.

Helping verbs are used both with action verbs and with linking verbs. The verb *to be* may be a helping verb or a linking verb, depending on how it is used.

EXAMPLES   He <u>was</u> hit on the head by an apple. (The helping verb *was,* a form of *to be,* is used with the action verb *hit.*)

By tomorrow, she <u>will have</u> been absent for three days. (The helping verbs *will* and *have* are used with the linking verb *been,* a form of *to be.*)

An adverb may come between a verb and its helping verb.

EXAMPLES   Janice <u>will</u> <u>surely</u> be on time today.

The chain <u>could</u> <u>too easily</u> be <u>broken</u> like that.

EXERCISE B   Underline the verbs in the following sentences, including any helping verbs. Be careful not to make any adverbs or complements part of the verbs. Circle *A* or *L* as before. (Add 5 points for each correct answer.)

A L   1. Lydia has eaten a dozen pancakes for breakfast.

A L   2. Seven jack-o-lanterns are too many for one Halloween.

A L   3. Fortunately, the ocean liner had not yet sailed.

A L   4. The key will be left in the glove compartment.

A L   5. Please do not give any more ties for the clothing drive.

A L   6. Our best friends may sometimes be our severest critics.

A L   7. She would probably have walked home along the river.

A L   8. The quarterback was taken out of the game because of heat prostration.

A L   9. The new school could not possibly be ready by then.

A L 10. Our last hope will otherwise be overlooked.

46

Finding the Direct Object

When the verb in a three-part sentence is an action verb, the third part of the sentence (the complement) is the part that receives the action of the verb. This receiver of the action is called a *direct object*.

A direct object is a complement, or completer, that receives the action of the verb or shows the result of the action.

In the following examples, the words printed in red are all direct objects.

EXAMPLES Her roses won an honorable **mention**

The boys dug a long, narrow **ditch**.

The earthquake broke **windows** and toppled **trees**.

Notice that a direct object occurs only after an action verb. To find the direct object in a sentence, ask *whom?* or *what?* after the verb. If you cannot find an answer to these test questions, the sentence does not have a direct object.

EXAMPLES The ferryboat hit a rock. (*Whom* or *what* did the ferryboat hit? *Rock* is the direct object.)

It sank near the shore. (*It sank*, the subject and verb, are complete by themselves. They do not have or need a complement.)

The direct object is never found in a prepositional phrase. If you apply the test questions with care, you will not be misled by sentences like these.

EXAMPLES Wilbur brought the **box** of cookies. (*Whom* or *what* did Wilbur bring? He brought the *box*.)

Evelyn found the **child** in the garage. (*Whom* or *what* did Evelyn find? She found the *child*.)

In question sentences, the direct object may come ahead of the verb.

EXAMPLES **What** did Wilbur bring?   **Whom** did Evelyn find?

EXERCISE A In each sentence, underline the subject once and the verb twice. Draw a line through each prepositional phrase. Then draw an arrow from the verb to the direct object. (Add 10 points for each correctly marked sentence.)

A. Mr. Wilcox had read some of the books.

1. They planted six beds of tulips in the garden.

2. A livid bolt of lightning split the tree down the middle.

3. The rain washed the topsoil away.

4. Geraldo recited the first paragraph of the Gettysburg Address.

5. The bus tires often scrape the curb.

6. The city put a fence of redwood planks along the road.

7. Naomi eagerly ate her oysters.

8. Our team successfully blocked the kick.

9. Karen and Lois both play the violin in the school orchestra.

10. The spy delivered the package of microfilm to the contact.

EXERCISE B Circle all the direct objects in the sentences below. *Caution:* not all of the sentences have direct objects. (Add 5 points for each correct answer.)

THE SECRET OF MIDAS

1 The ancient Greeks told a story about a musical contest between
2 the god Pan and the god Apollo. Pan played pipes of reed, and
3 Apollo played a silver lyre. Pan and Apollo sang songs, and then
4 they asked the listeners for a decision. The mountain god Tmolus
5 gave the award to Apollo, but Midas, the king of Lydia, preferred
6 Pan. Apollo was very angry. He changed Midas' ears into donkey's
7 ears. One should favor the strongest in contests between the gods.
8 Midas hid his ugly ears under his cap. His barber discovered the
9 dreadful secret. Midas threatened the barber with punishment if he
10 told. The barber could not resist the urge to tell. He dug a hole at
11 the river and then whispered the secret into the hole. He covered
12 the hole, with the secret in it, with earth. But reeds grew up there.
13 Every time the wind blew, the reeds whispered the secret of Midas.
14 "Midas has donkey's ears," said the reeds in a whisper. The whole
15 country eventually heard the secret, and Midas was covered with
16 shame. What did Midas do then? The story does not say. Perhaps
17 Apollo relented.

A Linking Verb Needs a Subject Complement

A group of words consisting of nothing but a subject and a linking verb does not ordinarily make much sense. Usually, a linking verb needs a third part to complete its meaning. This third part is what the linking verb links to the subject. Logically enough, it is called a *subject complement.*

A subject complement is a complement that describes, explains, or identifies the subject.

The subject complement may be a noun, a pronoun, or an adjective.

NOUN   Judy's mother is a **lawyer**. (*Lawyer* identifies the subject.)

PRONOUN   The winner of the election might well be **you**. (*You* identifies the subject.)

ADJECTIVE   I remain **sociable** with our former neighbors. (*Sociable* describes or explains the subject.)

The subject complement may be compound—made up of two or more words, usually connected by *and* or *or.*

EXAMPLE   Candace Bergen is both an actress and a photographer.

The following are often used as linking verbs.

COMMON LINKING VERBS

appear	become	grow	remain	smell	taste
be	feel	look	seem	sound	

Some verbs may be either action verbs or linking verbs, depending on how they are used.

LINKING VERBS   Lemonade **tastes** good.
                Mother **looked** beautiful.
ACTION VERBS   We all **tasted** the lemonade.
                Mother does not **look** in my diary.

EXERCISE A   Underline the subject complements in the sentences below. In the space to the left of each sentence write *n.* if the complement is a noun; *pron.* if it is a pronoun; or *adj.* if it is an adjective. If a sentence does not contain a subject complement, write *O* in the blank. (Add 10 points for each correctly marked sentence.)

adj. A. Yesterday morning was <u>disastrous</u> right from the beginning.

adj. 1. In the first place, the toast was <u>soggy.</u>

adj. 2. The cream tasted slightly <u>sour</u>.

pron. 3. The breakfast was not a good <u>one</u> in any way.

o. 4. The bus driver deliberately ignored <u>me.</u>

adj. 5. The next bus was an <u>express</u> and did not stop.

n. 6. It had become a real <u>crisis.</u>

o. 7. An unexpected <u>rainstorm</u> appeared from nowhere.

n. 8. I had forgotten my <u>umbrella.</u>

adj. 9. I felt more and more <u>unhappy.</u>

n. 10. It was a discouraging <u>morning</u>.

EXERCISE B Write the abbreviation *LV* or *AV* in the space to the left of each sentence, to show whether the italicized word is a *linking verb* or an *action verb*. (Add 10 points for each correct answer.)

A.V. 1. Ferdinand lazily *smelled* the flowers.

L.V. 2. The frying bacon and fresh toast *smelled* delicious.

L.V. 3. Imogene *appears* unusually cheerful this morning.

A.V. 4. An empty bus *appeared* suddenly at the end of the block.

L.V. 5. Because of her exercising, Anita *is growing* stronger.

L.V. 6. At a hint of fire, the principal *will sound* the alarm.

Complete the following sentences by writing an appropriate linking verb in the blank. Do not use the same verb twice.

A. Johnny Maxwell *must be* a very happy person.

7. Tomorrow *will be* a better day.

8. The moon *looks* bigger on the horizon.

9. On nice days I usually *feel* energetic.

10. Even from a distance, the Washington Monument *is* very tall.

Adverb or Adjective?

You may not always be sure whether to use the adjective form or the adverb form of a word. Two easy rules cover most such situations.

After a linking verb, use an adjective to modify the subject of the sentence.

After an action verb, use an adverb to modify the verb of the sentence.

EXAMPLES   That girl certainly looks **hungry**. (*Looks* is a linking verb and is followed therefore by the adjective *hungry*.)

That girl certainly eats **hungrily**. (*Eats* is an action verb and is followed therefore by the adverb *hungrily*.)

His manners are **bad**. (linking verb)

He chews his food **badly**. (action verb)

The most puzzling situations are likely to occur after words that can be either linking verbs or action verbs, depending on how they are used. In such cases you must be guided by the *meaning* of the verb. Does it indicate an action—something really happening—or does it simply connect the subject with its complement?

LINKING VERBS   She sounded very **cautious** to me. (*Cautious* modifies *she.*)

The water tasted **suspicious**. (*Suspicious* modifies *water.*)

ACTION VERBS   He sounded his horn **cautiously**. (*Cautiously* modifies *sounded.*)

The detective tasted the water **suspiciously**. (*Suspiciously* modifies *tasted.*)

EXERCISE A   In each of the following sentences, cross out the incorrect one of the two words in parentheses. (Add 10 points for each correct answer.)

1. He plays the piano very (beautiful, beautifully).

2. Maria, to our surprise, suddenly appeared (happy, happily).

3. Mrs. Kennedy got up and talked (brilliant, brilliantly).

4. That roast beef smells absolutely (delicious, deliciously).

5. Paying close attention, Maxine did the work very (skillful, skillfully).

6. The problem seems (clear, clearly) enough to me.

7. On her first try, she painted rather (crude, crudely).

8. The parachuter floated (gentle, gently) down to earth.

9. He reads very (quick, quickly).

10. A stranger appeared (sudden, suddenly) at the door with a message.

GOOD AND WELL

Distinguish between *good* and *well* as modifiers.

Use <u>good</u> to modify nouns and pronouns. Use <u>well</u> to modify verbs. <u>Good</u> is never used as an adverb.

NONSTANDARD   The pianist played very *good*. She is working out *good*.
STANDARD   The pianist played very **well**. She is working out **well**.

There is one case in which *well* is used as an adjective. This is when it means *in good health*.

STANDARD   She feels **well** now.   (She no longer feels sick.)
ALSO STANDARD   She felt **good** after her exhilarating swim.

EXERCISE B   Cross out the incorrect word in each of these sentences. (Add 10 points for each correct answer.)

1. The old sailor certainly whittles (good, well).

2. After so many lessons, he finally drives (good, well).

3. In the darkness of the cave, they couldn't see very (good, well).

4. Everybody eats (good, well) on board an ocean liner.

5. No airplane could serve its passengers so (good, well).

6. Aunt Martha was seriously ill, but she is now quite (good, well).

7. From your description, that movie certainly sounds (good, well).

8. Everything you do must be done (good, well).

9. The stream looks (good, well), but it may still be polluted.

10. A cold shower seems especially (good, well) at the end of a hot day.

Chapter Review

EXERCISE A   Underline the verb in each sentence (including helping verbs), and then, if it is an action verb, write *AV* in the space provided at the left; or, if it is a linking verb, write *LV* in the space. (Add 10 points for each correctly marked sentence.)

...... 1. A man gathered mussels from a brook near Paterson, New Jersey, in 1857.

...... 2. Many hard objects were found in the cooked mussels.

...... 3. These objects certainly appeared worthless.

...... 4. He threw some of them away.

...... 5. Then he grew thoughtful.

...... 6. He appeared at a jeweler's house with the remaining uncooked mussels.

...... 7. The jeweler gave him about $30 for all the remaining mussels.

...... 8. He felt excited by his unexpected good fortune.

...... 9. Eventually one of these pearls was sold to Tiffany & Co. for $900.

...... 10. Later this same pearl was purchased by an empress.

EXERCISE B   In each of the following sentences, cross out the word in parentheses that is incorrect. (Add 10 points for each correct answer.)

1. The opera singer's voice sounded (good, well) last night.
2. My brother still types (bad, badly) despite six weeks of practice.
3. He reacted very (sudden, suddenly) to my suggestion.
4. After two weeks of the flu, Sara finally feels (good, well) again.
5. These roses smell (sweet, sweetly).
6. Sandra does everything (well, good).
7. Come (quick, quickly)! I smell smoke.
8. I felt (good, well) after our swim.
9. I can finish this homework (easy, easily) by nine o'clock.
10. Even with glasses, Grandpa doesn't see (well, good).

EXERCISE C In the following paragraph, underline the subject of each sentence once and the verb twice. Circle each complement. In the space after each sentence, write a *2* if the sentence has a two-part base and a *3* if it has a three-part base. (Add 2 points for each correct answer.)

1 The Pawnee Indians tell a pretty story about the origin of the wild
2 flower larkspur. (. . . .) Dream Woman is a Pawnee goddess. (. . . .)
3 She lives on the other side of the sky. (. . . .) One day, the earth
4 people attracted her attention. (. . . .) She became curious about their
5 activities. (. . . .) She cut a hole in the sky and made a stalk for use
6 as a ladder. (. . . .) The stalk was fashioned out of the green material
7 lining the sky. (. . . .) A few flecks of the outside blue stuck to it
8 also. (. . . .) Dream Woman descended the stalk. (. . . .) But it was
9 brittle from exposure to the sun. (. . . .) It broke into thousands of
10 pieces under her weight. (. . . .) The scattered pieces became
11 larkspur. (. . . .) Some people call larkspur by the name *delphinium.*
12 (. . . .)

EXERCISE D In the following paragraph, underline the direct objects once and circle the subject complements. Some sentences have more than one complement. (Add 5 points for each correct answer.)

1 Merlin, the magician, once lent his magic wand to young Prince
2 Arthur for a while. The wand was very powerful. Arthur used it for
3 his own private purposes. Arthur's nurse called him for dinner. He
4 was not hungry in the least. He promptly transformed her into a crow.
5 She felt ridiculous in a tree and scolded him loudly from her perch.
6 Arthur mocked her and offered some kernels of corn to her. He did
7 not fear a crow. Eventually, Merlin came in search of the nurse. Arthur
8 denied any knowledge of her whereabouts. Merlin was wise and knew
9 Arthur's tricks. "You," said Merlin immediately, "are a liar!" Arthur
10 could not fool Merlin. Merlin promptly took back his magic wand.
11 He changed the crow back into the nurse. The nurse remained
12 indignant and quite rightly sent Arthur to bed without any supper.

Cumulative Review

A Underline the subject of each sentence once and the verb twice. Include all parts of compound subjects and verbs. (Add 5 points for each correct answer.)

MIGHTY RIVERS OF AFRICA

1   The Nile and the Congo are the longest rivers in Africa. The Nile
2 flows through the desert and empties into the Mediterranean. The
3 Congo makes a great loop through the jungle and flows into the
4 Atlantic. Most of Egypt's water for irrigation and for sanitation comes
5 from the Nile. Egypt has a dry climate and depends on the Nile for
6 a livelihood. The Congo and its neighbors have a very wet climate.
7 Some of the world's heaviest rainfalls and some of the thickest jungles
8 can be observed on the west coast of Africa.

B Write the letter *a*, *b*, *c*, or *d* in front of each sentence to explain what kind of sentence it is according to the following code. (Add 10 points for each correct answer.)

a—simple sentence with compound subject
b—simple sentence with compound verb
c—simple sentence with compound subject and compound verb
d—compound sentence

...... 1. My sister and I go hiking in the woods or try water-skiing at the beach as often as possible.

...... 2. Unfortunately, we cannot do both at the same time, and no one else can, either.

...... 3. Sometimes I want to go hiking and she wants to water-ski.

...... 4. Then we argue and squabble about it.

...... 5. She prefers water-skiing, but I like hiking better.

...... 6. We can always flip a coin and make up our minds that way.

...... 7. Dad and Mom both enjoy water-skiing but have little interest in hiking.

...... 8. Hiking near an isolated lake with a powerful motorboat available would be an ideal vacation for us, but it is not too likely.

..... 9. Secluded hiking trails and gasoline-powered sports do not usually go together.

..... 10. For my part, I enjoy the silence of the deep woods and regret the shortness of our hiking trips in them.

C   Over each word in italics write one of the following abbreviations to identify its part of speech: *n.* for nouns; *pron.* for pronouns; *adj.* for adjectives; *v.* for verbs; *adv.* for adverbs; and *prep.* for prepositions. (Add 2 points for each correct answer.)

INDUSTRIAL HISTORY

1   Railroads were *invented* in England over a century ago. *They*
2   resulted from *experiments* in moving coal *from* the *mine* to the factory
3   *economically*. George Stephenson's *remarkable* locomotive *was* the
4   *first* one ever made. *His* invention put *stage* coaches and canals out
5   of *business*. *Within twenty* years, England was *covered* by a network
6   *of* railroads. The economic *boom* accompanying *railway* construction
7   *caused* speculation in stocks of the new companies and made *some*
8   *people* rich and *others* poor. At *almost* the *same* time the telegraph
9   was invented by an American. *Telegraph* systems made long-distance
10   railroads and *fast* trains possible by providing a *means* of quick and
11   reliable *signal* control. The *steamship* was a *later* development. *Wood*
12   passed out of *favor* for boat-building and was replaced by iron. The
13   *demand* for iron rails and iron ships caused a great *expansion* in
14   England's *iron* and *steel* industry. *For* many years, England was by
15   far the world's *leading* producer of *iron*. Not *until* the *twentieth*
16   century did the United States *pass* England *in* steel production. As
17   the automobile *developed,* steel *manufacture* increased even *more,* and
18   *today* the *car* makers are the largest buyers of *steel,* both *here* and
19   in England.

Building Vocabulary: Getting Meaning from Context

You generally meet an unfamiliar word in a context of some kind —surrounded by other words (the *verbal context*) whose meaning you already know. The words you know give clues to the meaning of the new word. If you can interpret these clues like good word detectives, you can often guess the meaning of the unfamiliar word.

The verbal context provides clues to the meanings of unfamiliar words.

Suppose that at first glance you are not sure what the word *impoverished* means in the following sentence.

EXAMPLE   The **impoverished** tenants were no longer able to pay their rent.

The rest of the sentence suggests that *impoverish* must have something to do with not having enough money—not even enough for something as necessary as rent. *Poor* would be a good guess at the meaning of *impoverished.*

Caution: Check your context guesses by looking up the words in a dictionary, both to make sure you are right about the meanings and to find other, related meanings.

EXERCISE   Each of the words printed in red is followed by a passage in which it is used. Work out the meaning of each word from its context. Then, in the space to the left of each word write the number of the meaning that fits this context, from the list of meanings given on page 58. (Add 10 points for each correct answer.)

WORDS IN CONTEXT

.... **inflammable** /in flám ə bə-l/, *adj.*   At one time, most gasoline trucks dragged a short length of chain behind them to ground sparks that might endanger their *inflammable* contents.

.... **extinct** /ik stíngkt/, *adj.*   The passenger pigeon is one of the best examples of a species that has become *extinct* because of hunters. In recent years, the whooping crane has become nearly *extinct,* but may yet survive.

.... **refute** /ri fy-ū́t/, *v.*   Janine claimed that the pioneering spirit was dead in America. We easily *refuted* her with examples of people in modern life who had shown the independent spirit of the pioneers.

.... **concise** /kən sĭs/, *adj.* Mr. Watson asked me to make my themes more *concise*. He pointed out that there is no virtue in using two words where only one is needed.

.... **coincide** /kṓ in sĭd/, *v.* My spring vacation did not *coincide* with Bernice's this year. Her vacation began a week earlier than mine.

.... **eject** /i jékt/, *v.* The plane was equipped with a lever which set off a small charge of explosives, *ejecting* the pilot from the crippled plane.

.... **asset** /ás et/, *n.* Marjorie may not be the smartest person in the class, but she gets the best grades. A willingness to work hard is her great *asset*.

.... **distort** /dis tórt/, *v.* A newspaper may *distort* the truth by printing a candidate's remarks out of context. The warrior's face was *distorted* by rage.

.... **catastrophe** /kə tás trə fē/, *n.* The San Francisco earthquake, which was followed by a fire, was a terrible *catastrophe*.

.... **compensate** /kóm pən sāt/, *v.* The waiter felt that the customer's tip did not *compensate* him for the efforts he had made. Keen hearing may *compensate* a blind person for loss of sight.

WORD MEANINGS

1. *Singular:* Anything of value belonging to a person or business. *Plural:* Everything belonging to a person or business that might be turned into money with which to pay debts.
2. A sudden and complete disaster; a great misfortune.
3. To happen at the same time.
4. To pay someone for something, especially a service; to make up for something lost or damaged.
5. Brief; saying much in a few words.
6. To twist out of shape; of ideas, to make false in some way, to give a wrong impression of.
7. To throw or drive out suddenly by force.
8. No longer living or active; of species of animals without living descendants.
9. Easily set on fire.
10. To disprove a person or a person's views by giving arguments or evidence against them.

REVIEW EXERCISE In the space to the left of each question write the lettered word that best explains the word in italics. (Add 25 points for each correct answer.)

.... 1. If you *adhere* to an idea, do you (a) favor or (b) oppose it?

.... 2. If you are *agitated* in your mind, are you (a) peaceful or (b) upset?

.... 3. Would an *exquisite* work of art be (a) beautiful or (b) ugly?

.... 4. Would a *humane* action be (a) kind or (b) cruel?

Spelling: Three Sounds of <u>ea</u>

A letter combination that causes many spelling problems is *ea.* This pair of vowels is troublesome because it is used to represent several vowel sounds.

Pronounce the words in the three word groups below:

1	*2*	*3*
pl**ea**sure	t**ea**ch	st**ea**k
h**ea**ven	app**ea**l	gr**ea**t

Try to identify the three different sounds of *ea* illustrated by the three word groups. In group *1, ea* sounds like /e/; in group *2,* like /ē/; in group *3,* like /ā/. This confusion exists because spelling has not changed to keep pace with changes in pronunciation. About a thousand years ago, during the period when Old English was spoken, both the *e* and the *a* in *ea* were sounded. The word *heaven,* for example, probably sounded something like this: /há ə fen/. (The /f/ sound was often changed to a /v/ sound through the centuries.) Another example of the lag between spelling and pronunciation can be seen in the words in group *3.* In Shakespeare's time, /ā/ was commonly spelled *ea,* and a word like *deal* was pronounced /dāl/.

Thus, the English language retains many old spellings even though they no longer represent the way the words are pronounced now. You must therefore memorize the spellings of such words as *pleasure, teach,* and *steak.* You will notice that very few common *ea* words retain the /ā/ sound.

EXERCISE A   The *ea* in each word below has one of the three sounds we have been studying. Between the slanted lines next to each word, indicate the sound of the *ea* in that word by writing e, ē, or ā. (Add 10 points for each correct answer.)

1. ready   ...... / .... / ......
2. treaty   ...... / .... / ......
3. weather   ...... / .... / ......
4. seal   ...... / .... / ......
5. yea   ..... / .... / ......

6. leather   ...... / .... / ......
7. reason   ...... / .... / ......
8. ahead   ...... / .... / ......
9. break   ...... / .... / ......
10. disease   ...... / .... / ......

EXERCISE B   Write five words (other than those given in this lesson) in which *ea* is pronounced /e/, and five words in which it is pronounced /ē/. (Add 10 points for each correct answer.)

/e/ /ē/

....
....
....
....
....

EXERCISE C Write a paragraph (it can be humorous) using all of the /e/ and /ē/ words from Exercise B and as many words in which /ā/ is spelled *ea* as can be worked in. Underscore all *ea* words.

....
....
....
....
....
....
....
....
....

REVIEW EXERCISE Write *ie* or *ei*, whichever is correct, in the blank space in each word below. (Add 5 points for each correct answer.)

1. n . . . . ghborly
2. pr . . . . st
3. h . . . . ght
4. bel . . . . ve
5. gr . . . . ve
6. w . . . . rd
7. shr . . . . k
8. l . . . . sure
9. w . . . . ght
10. s . . . . zure

11. n . . . . ther
12. perc . . . . ve
13. c . . . . ling
14. conc . . . . ted
15. misch . . . . f
16. for . . . . gner
17. br . . . . f
18. sh . . . . ld
19. gr . . . . f
20. rec . . . . ve

CHAPTER FOUR

Building with Prepositional Phrases

In the following sentence, the two word groups printed in italics are prepositional phrases:

After a long, hard search, Henry found his bike *in the ditch.*

It would be difficult to express these same ideas in any other way, without using the two prepositional phrases. Very often, by means of prepositional phrases, you can say things which you cannot say half so well in any other way. The prepositional phrase is one of the most useful tools in ENGLISH WORKSHOP, both for saying what you mean and for making what you say clear and interesting. In this chapter, you will study the formation and uses of the prepositional phrase.

LESSON 31

What Is a Prepositional Phrase?

A *preposition* is a word that shows a relationship between the noun or pronoun that follows it and some other word in the sentence. The preposition and its noun or pronoun together is called a *prepositional phrase.* Words like *of, for, with, from, through, near, since,* and *under* can all be used as prepositions.

What makes a phrase so useful is that it is a whole group of words that can be used like a single part of speech in a sentence. Notice the groups of words printed in red in these sentences.

EXAMPLES   Has anyone seen the girl **with red hair**? (used as an adjective to modify the noun *girl*)
The cat raced **down the stairs**. (used as an adverb to modify the verb *raced,* telling where the cat raced)

A prepositional phrase may consist of just two words—a preposition and a noun or pronoun.

EXAMPLES   **near** home   **of** cookies   **without** you   **beside** her

The noun or pronoun may also have modifiers, in which case the prepositional phrase may contain several words.

EXAMPLES   **after** a heavy rain   **beyond** the rugged, snow-covered mountains

61

A single sentence may contain several prepositional phrases strung together, one after the other. Prepositional phrases are often used in this way for descriptive purposes.

EXAMPLE   The king entered **to** the accompaniment **of** a blaring fanfare **from** the massed bugles and side drums.

EXERCISE A Put parentheses around all the prepositional phrases in the following sentences. (Add 10 points for each correctly marked sentence.)

A. Baseball became a popular sport (after the War)(Between the States).

1. Baseball (in the late 1800's) was very different (from today's game)

2. Early pitchers played (without gloves.)

3. (During a long, difficult game) a pitcher's hand (often became bruised.)

4. The first glove was worn (during a game)(in 1875.)

5. Charles C. Waite wore the glove (in this game)(for protection.)

6. The players (without gloves) ridiculed him.

7. His glove was flesh-colored (with a large opening)(in the back)(for ventilation.)

8. Soon other pitchers were playing (with a glove.)

9. (After a while) pads were placed (inside the glove)(for cushioning.)

10. Wire masks were first worn (by catchers)(in a game)(at Boston)(during the 1875–76 season.)

EXERCISE B Put parentheses around the twenty prepositional phrases in the following paragraph. Some phrases are quite long. Be sure to include all parts. (Add 5 points for each correct answer.)

1   (Across the bay) cottages (of whitewashed stone) straggled (along the
2   road)(toward the pier.) Children played (under the trees) and bought ice
3   cream and ices (from local stands.) Dogs rested (in the shade)(by the
4   children.) Every day (on the stroke)(of ten) the boat (from the mainland
5   docked there)(with passengers) and long-awaited mail and was greeted)
6   (by a crowd)(of local citizens and visitors.) The wave-tossed boat crashed
7   (against the pilings)(of the pier,) and the crowd cheered the bravery (of
8   the captain.) Once again she had brought her vessel safely (to port)(with a
9   load)(of free-spending but seasick tourists.)

62   © 1977 HBJ

The Adjective Phrase

An **adjective phrase** is a prepositional phrase that is used as an adjective to modify a noun or a pronoun.

ADJECTIVES	ADJECTIVE PHRASES
a very **strong** person	a person **of great strength**
a **rudderless** ship	a ship **without a rudder**

Like an adjective, an adjective phrase modifies a noun or pronoun by making its meaning more definite. Usually the adjective phrase answers the question *what kind?* or *which one?*

WHAT KIND? Edith Hamilton has written books **about folklore and mythology**. (what kind of books? books *about folklore and mythology*)

WHICH ONE? The building **behind the burning house** was saved. (which building? the building *behind the burning house*)

Notice that if the underlined nouns in the sentences above are replaced by pronouns, the phrases then modify the pronouns.

EXAMPLES Edith Hamilton has written some **about folklore and mythology**.

The one **behind the burning house** was saved.

EXERCISE A Put parentheses around each adjective phrase in the following sentences and draw an arrow to the noun or pronoun it modifies. (Add 5 points for each correctly marked sentence.)

A. The sound (of falling rain) can be very soothing.

1. The woman (in the blue coat) suddenly stood up.

2. The family (across the street) just adopted two children.

3. Marjorie composes music (for her favorite poems.)

4. Somebody robbed the old-fashioned house (with the wide porch)

5. The Perezes triumphantly served tomatoes (from their own garden.)

6. Books (from the public library) covered her desk.

7. That huge mahogany table (in the hall) is much too large.

8. A smaller one (with a convenient drawer) would be more suitable.

9. They brought home a few (of every shape and size.)

10. Patricia wanted a ticket (for the football game.)

11. Someone (from Porlock) rang the doorbell and interrupted him.

12. The waiter brought them a check (for somebody else's meal.)

13. This motel has a sauna, but the one (down the street) has a swimming pool.

14. Nothing (under the sun) could make me do it.

15. The bay (off Rye) is sometimes oily.

16. A cave (below the cliff) sheltered them.

17. He brought home a mixed basket (of apples and pears.)

18. They dug a large crescent-shaped bed (for zinnias.)

19. The museum has a very old Navajo rug (with an intricate design.)

20. She wolfed her three thin slices (of whole wheat bread.)

EXERCISE B Write a suitable adjective phrase in the blank in each sentence. The phrase should modify the noun or pronoun that comes immediately before it. (Add 10 points for each correct phrase.)

A. An old house .... *near the glen* .... caught fire last night.

1. In the safe was a black box ... *under the money* ....

2. The announcer ..... *on the stage* ..... mispronounced the sponsor's name.

3. Last week we attended the game .. *until eleven o'clock.*

4. The one .... *behind the car* ...... belongs to me.

5. Some .. *beneath the tree* ... are members of that club.

6. That new car ...... *over there* ..... belongs to Aunt Cathy.

7. Mr. Poitier has just returned from a trip .. *around the* ... *world.* ....

8. Everyone ...... *in Florida* .... has been vaccinated.

9. A house .... *up here* .... is no place to raise a family.

10. Finally, the child selected three .. *from the rack* .....

64

The Adverb Phrase

An <u>adverb phrase</u> is a prepositional phrase that is used as an adverb to modify a verb.*

Like adverbs, prepositional phrases may answer the question *when? where? how? why?* or *how much? (how long? how often?)*

EXAMPLES   He hid the money in a tin can. (*Where* did he hide the money? He hid it *in a tin can.*)
I did my shopping after school. (*When?*)
I painted the chair in too big a hurry. (*How?*)
They were scattering the papers for fun. (*Why?*)
That milk bottle has been there for two days. (*How long?*)

Adverb phrases also answer a great many other questions.

EXAMPLES   I thought of you today.
The house was built of brick.
He wrote a very nice thank-you note to the minister.
He had replaced the old machine with a newer model.

Almost any adverb can be replaced with an adverb phrase.

ADVERB	ADVERB PHRASE
She campaigned **actively**.	She campaigned **in an active way**.
They left **hastily**.	They left **in haste**.
They got along **well**.	They got along **in a satisfactory way**.

Straightforward adverbs are often preferable to adverb phrases, but the phrase has one great advantage over the ordinary adverb: because the object of the preposition is a noun or a pronoun, adjectives (and adverbs modifying these adjectives) can be put into the phrase. With these extra modifiers, the phrase can have a much more precise meaning than a single adverb by itself.

EXAMPLES   She campaigned in a **dignified** and **active** way.

They left in **great** but rather **dangerous** haste.

---

*Adverb phrases are also occasionally used to modify adjectives or adverbs.

EXERCISE A Put parentheses around each adverb phrase in the sentences below, and draw an arrow to the word it modifies. (Add 10 points for each correctly marked sentence.)

A. The congresswoman unexpectedly called (at our house).

1. She was campaigning (for a third term).

2. She was accompanied (by news photographers and radio announcers.)

3. My father and mother have known the congresswoman (for many years.)

4. The photographers took our pictures (with great enthusiasm.)

5. Meanwhile, the congresswoman was talking politics (with my parents.)

6. The congresswoman left (after about fifteen minutes.)

7. We were all dazed (by this sudden visit.)

8. The paper printed our picture (in this morning's edition.)

9. Several friends telephoned my parents (in surprise.)

10. Naturally, my parents supported the congresswoman (in this election.)

EXERCISE B Enclose all the prepositional phrases below in parentheses. Then, in the blank at the left, write *adj.* if the phrase is an adjective phrase and *adv.* if it is an adverb phrase. (Add 10 points for each correctly marked sentence.)

adv. 1. Kitty watched the parade (from an upstairs window.)

adj. 2. Ms. Etler wrote a book (about nuclear physics.)

adj. 3. The chef made chocolate éclairs (with ice cream filling.)

adv. 4. I delivered the sealed envelope (in a hurry.)

adv. 5. Mr. Sanford directed the play (during Mrs. Knight's absence.)

adv. 6. The whole family went (to the homecoming game.)

adv. 7. They didn't leave (until one o'clock.)

adj. 8. The pictures (in the locked file) are missing.

adv. 9. The mayor always greets people (with a big smile.)

adv. 10. A prefabricated plastic-coated cardboard house has been proposed (by an ingenious industrial designer.)

Put the Phrase Where It Makes Good Sense!

A misplaced phrase can spoil the effectiveness of a sentence and even change its meaning. To get full usefulness from prepositional phrases, you must develop a feeling for their placement in sentences.

The usual position for a prepositional phrase is after the word it modifies.

ADJECTIVE PHRASE   Arnold told a story **about fishing**.

ADVERB PHRASE   Arnold told a story **in the elevator**.

The two sentences above make good sense as they stand. If you try to combine them, however, you come out with two phrases in the same sentence, and if you are not careful they can make trouble for you.

UNCLEAR   Arnold told a story about fishing *in the elevator.*

Where did Arnold's fishing take place? In speaking, you use your voice to set off the phrase *in the elevator* from the rest of the sentence. In writing, however, the placement of this phrase makes it seem, at first glance, to modify *fishing.* But it is the telling of the story, not the fishing, that takes place in the elevator. The difficulty can be cleared up by moving the out-of-place phrase to the head of the sentence.

CLEAR   **In the elevator** Arnold told a story about fishing.

An adjective phrase must nearly always come right after the word it modifies. An adverb phrase, however, may be moved about quite freely, often to the beginning of the sentence. If a sentence with two or more phrases sounds wrong to you, follow these steps to make the meaning clear: (1) Notice which words the phrases modify. Does the placement of an adverb phrase make it seem to modify the wrong word? (2) Try the adverb phrase in a different spot in the sentence, especially at the beginning.

Even if both phrases are adjective phrases, we must make sure they are really saying what we want them to say. For example, how would you put these sentence parts together?

Caroline read a book   about a murder   on the Boston train

The phrase *on the Boston train* could be an adjective phrase modifying *murder.* If so, it should follow the word *murder* (as above), meaning that the book Caroline read told about a murder that took place on the Boston train. If you take *on the Boston train* to be an adverb phrase modifying *read,* you would mean something quite different (Caroline read her book while riding on the Boston train). You can show this different meaning by putting the phrase at the beginning of a sentence. There, since it has no earlier noun to modify, the phrase must be an adverb phrase.

EXAMPLE   On the Boston train Caroline read a book about a murder.

EXERCISE   The following sentences contain phrases that do not make good sense in their present locations. Underline each misplaced phrase and show by a caret mark (∧) where the phrase ought to go. (Add 10 points for each correctly marked sentence.)

A. Sherry rode her bike past the police officer with no hands.

1. The truckers drove all day without rest in the pouring rain.

2. Jim told Mrs. Warren about the icebox in the rowboat.

3. Mr. Jefferson lectured about bridge construction in the auditorium.

4. Edythe could smell dinner in the oven on the porch.

5. Joan told Annie about the aircraft carrier in the library.

6. They built a house for the family with three chimneys.

Rewrite the following groups of words in good sentences, placing each phrase where it makes good sense.

7. the guard at the main switch   7. . . . .
   turned the power off   . . . .
   on duty   . . . .

8. Harriet for new experiences   8. . . . .
   by her enthusiasm   . . . .
   is often carried away   . . . .

9. they took the puppy   9. . . . .
   with air vents   . . . .
   in a portable kennel   . . . .

10. Maria watches the sailboats   10. . . . .
    from the shady porch   . . . .
    in the glittering sunlight   . . . .
    of the Riverview Sailing Club   . . . .

Chapter Review

EXERCISE A Underline all the prepositional phrases in the following paragraph. (Add 4 points for each correct answer.)

GRACE WILEY'S SNAKES

1   Most people picture themselves with interesting careers. Some
2   want jobs that take them outside the realm of ordinary experience.
3   Grace Wiley had such a career. She was a handler of snakes. She
4   had one of the world's largest collections. She kept her snakes in the
5   barn behind her house and would show them to tourists. Inside the
6   barn were cages with vipers, rattlesnakes, fer-de-lances, karaits, and
7   cobras. Throughout the world people have at the same time feared
8   and revered cobras. Cobras are very large snakes which come from
9   Asia or Africa. They have around their neck a loose fold of skin
10   that expands into a hood upon excitation. Grace Wiley studied the
11   cobras in her collection and learned about their habits. During the
12   attack the cobra rears straight upward. A hand held above the
13   standing cobra's head is outside its range. The cobra must bite
14   through its victim's skin and chew rather than simply strike it.
15   Grace Wiley often let a cobra hit against her flattened palm. As
16   long as the cobra couldn't grab and chew, it couldn't insert its
17   venom into the blood.

EXERCISE B Put parentheses around the prepositional phrases in the following sentences and draw an arrow from the phrase to the word it modifies. (Add 4 points for each correct answer.)

1. Many ancient peoples had similar stories about the sky.

2. In one African folktale, the sky is supported by two gods.

3. Libanja supports the eastern part with a pole, and Songo supports the western part.

4. Without their aid, the sky would fall, and people would become lizards.

5. Early Scandinavians also looked with concern at the sky.

6. One ancient tale tells of a mighty ash tree called *Yggdrasil*.

7. All of the universe is supported by this tree.

8. Its three great roots reach into the regions of the gods, of the giants, and of darkness and cold.

9. A serpent with a great hunger gnaws continuously at its root.

10. One day the tree may fall, and the universe may come crashing onto the heads of people.

11. The Greek god Zeus fought with skill and daring for control of the universe.

12. He punished his enemy Atlas in a severe manner.

13. Atlas bears the weight of the world on his back and separates the heavens from the earth.

EXERCISE C Put parentheses around the prepositional phrases in the sentences below. Above each phrase write *adj.* for an adjective phrase (modifying a noun or pronoun) and *adv.* for an adverb phrase (modifying a verb). (Add 5 points for each correct answer.)

1. The trail to camp follows the river.

2. Veronica ran swiftly to camp and told her news.

3. The commander sent messengers to all the neighboring garrisons.

4. The enemy proceeded cautiously through the mountain passes and approached the settlements on the plains.

5. A stitch in time is not worth nine.

6. The line of least resistance may not be the shortest distance between two points.

7. The night attack took the enemy by surprise.

8. The new facts about the housing project presented a different viewpoint.

Cumulative Review

A In the following paragraph, underline each subject once and each verb twice. Watch out for compound subjects and verbs. (Add 4 points for each correct answer.)

SURPRISE

1   Mary Kilpatrick and her mother laid plans for a surprise party
2   for Mary's father. This year, Mr. Kilpatrick's birthday fell on a
3   Sunday, and Mary and Mrs. Kilpatrick were making an occasion of
4   it. Several of Mary's aunts and uncles live not far away. Every one
5   of them was invited to the party. They would bring their families.
6   The whole party was planned well in advance, and Mr. Kilpatrick
7   knew nothing about it. At three in the afternoon of Mr. Kilpatrick's
8   birthday, the guests made a rendezvous in their cars just around the
9   corner, out of sight. Then all of the cars drove up at once, and people
10   piled out and surprised Mr. Kilpatrick.

B Above each of the italicized words in the following paragraph write one of these abbreviations to show its part of speech: *n.* for noun; *v.* for verb; *pron.* for pronoun; *prep.* for preposition; *adv.* for adverb; and *adj.* for adjective. (Add 2 points for each correct answer.)

NAPOLEON'S DOWNFALL

1   *In* the year 1812, Napoleon *invaded Russia with* an army of *over*
2   530,000 men. *He entered* Russia in *June* and began the *long* march
3   *toward* Moscow. He *would* cover *every* mile of the *way laboriously*
4   *on* foot. The *Russian* army retreated *slowly before* Napoleon, but
5   *finally made* a *stand* at the city of *Borodino.* The battle of Borodino,
6   in September, 1812, *was* the *bloodiest battle* Napoleon had *fought*
7   up to *that* time. The *Russians* were defeated, and one week *later*
8   Napoleon *occupied* Moscow. The *next* day, Moscow *mysteriously*
9   began to burn. Napoleon had *only* 100,000 men in Moscow. *His* army
10   was *dangerously* drawn out *along* the line of *communication with*

11   France. The Russian *tsar* refused to surrender. *Winter* came on
12   *quickly.* Napoleon was *forced* to retreat. *Under attack by* the Russians
13   and the *terrible* winter, Napoleon's army *gradually dissolved.* Over
14   500,000 of France's *finest* soldiers were *permanently* lost. The back-
15   bone of Napoleon's power was broken.

C   In the following paragraph, underline every direct object once and
circle every subject complement. If in doubt, find the verb in the sentence
and notice whether it is an *action verb* or a *linking verb.* Remember that
an action verb takes a direct object, while a linking verb is followed by
a subject complement. (Add 5 points for each correct answer.)

TRAGIC MELODY

1   The famous composer Schumann lived an unfortunate life. As a
2   young man he injured his hand and therefore could not become a
3   concert pianist. He fell in love with a talented woman. Her father
4   at first forbade her marriage to Schumann but later changed his
5   mind. Her name was Clara. Later, she became the most famous
6   woman pianist of the nineteenth century. Schumann wrote some of
7   his finest music immediately after his marriage. These were the
8   happiest days of his life. He gave several great songs to Clara as
9   presents. Then, for many years, he was a very successful composer.
10   But suddenly, one day, he heard a note in his ear. It was a halluci-
11   nation. This was the first sign of mental collapse. Clara got the best
12   possible care for him, but his health failed. He grew despondent and
13   attempted suicide. Finally, Clara sent him to a hospital, where he
14   died. Later, the composer Brahms, although much younger, loved
15   Clara, but she rejected him, and Brahms never married.

Building Vocabulary: Using the Dictionary

When you meet a new word in reading or conversation, the context alone may not show the word's precise meaning, or it may show only one of several meanings which the word may have. In such a case you naturally check your context guess against a good dictionary.

Use a dictionary as a tool for building your vocabulary.

Merely looking up a new word in a dictionary is usually not enough to build the word into your vocabulary. To make the most of the help which a dictionary can give, you need to use it systematically.

1. Note the word's spelling, pronunciation, and part of speech. Check the *pronunciation key* if you are not sure how the word is pronounced.

2. Copy the word in the vocabulary section of your notebook. (Dividing the word in syllables, as in the dictionary, will help you master its spelling.)

3. In your notebook, give the context in which you first read or heard the word.

4. Copy the word's meaning or meanings.

5. Write a sentence of your own to illustrate the meaning or meanings given for the word in the dictionary.

Step 5 is especially important. Until you know a word well enough to recognize it in a new context and use it in your own writing and speaking, you have not really made the word part of your vocabulary.

WORD MEANING   **commodity**: (1) anything useful; (2) anything bought and sold.

ILLUSTRATION   Fresh vegetables are one of the few **commodities** that drugstores do not sell.

EXERCISE   Look up the words below in a dictionary and supply the following information about each word: (1) Pronunciation: divide the word into syllables. (2) Illustration: study the definition and then write a short sentence illustrating the chief meaning of the word. Notice the example. Be sure that your sentence illustrates the meaning of the word in the part of speech indicated, since some words on the list may be used as two different parts of speech. (Add 5 points for each correct item.)

aggressive, *adj.* (1). *ag-gres-sive* (2) *an aggressive person likes to pick a fight.*

audible, *adj.* (1). . . . . (2). . . . .

. . . .

eloquent, *adj.* (1)................ (2)............................

....

fantastic, *adj.* (1)................ (2)............................

....

hamper, *v.* (1)................ (2)............................

....

homicide, *n.* (1)................ (2)............................

....

monopoly, *n.* (1)................ (2)............................

....

rebuke, *v.* (1)................ (2)............................

....

repel, *v.* (1)................ (2)............................

....

salient, *adj.* (1)................ (2)............................

....

vivid, *adj.* (1)................ (2)............................

....

REVIEW EXERCISE In the space to the left of each word in the left-hand column write the letter of the best meaning for that word. (Add 10 points for each correct answer.)

.... 1. coincide   a. to reimburse

.... 2. refute   b. capable of being set afire

.... 3. distort   c. having no living successors

.... 4. eject   d. compact, terse

.... 5. inflammable   e. to be in the same place

.... 6. compensate   f. a useful or valuable thing

.... 7. extinct   g. to make crooked

.... 8. asset   h. a sudden disaster

.... 9. concise   i. to throw out

.... 10. catastrophe   j. to disprove

Spelling: A Trio of Confusing Prefixes: pre-, pro-, per-

Words that begin with *pre-*, *pro-*, and *per-* are confusing because these three prefixes from the Latin both look and sound so much alike. There are two things you can do to avoid misspellings when writing a word that contains one of these troublesome prefixes. First, you can *pronounce* the word very carefully. Try to say the word, especially the prefix, with great preciseness. Say *pre*caution, *pro*motion, *per*suade.

A second way to avoid confusion is by learning the *meaning* of each prefix, along with a simple, clearly understood word containing that prefix. Try to memorize the meaning (or meanings) of each prefix below and the example word that illustrates it.

PREFIX	MEANING	EXAMPLE
pre-	*before*	**pre**arrange (arrange before)
pro-	*forward*	**pro**mote (move forward)
per-	*through* / *thorough*	**per**colate (seep through) / **per**fect (thoroughly done)

EXERCISE A   In the blank in each sentence below, write the word whose meaning is given in parentheses. Each word you write should begin with *pre-*, *pro-*, or *per-*. (Add 20 points for each correct answer.)

1. The letter *g* . . . . the letter *h* in the alphabet.   (comes before)

2. A jet plane does not have a . . . .   (rotating blade device)

3. What does the weather forecaster . . . . for tomorrow? (foretell)

4. Don't try to . . . . this meeting, please.   (lengthen in time)

5. Lynn is the . . . . leader of this committee.   (continuing)

EXERCISE B   In the blank, add *pre-*, *pro-*, or *per-* to each word or word part below. Be sure that the new word you make has the meaning given in parentheses. (Add 20 points for each correct answer.)

EXAMPLE   . . . *pre*war (before the war)

1. . . . . . . .suppose (suppose before)

2. . . . . . . .fessor (one who puts knowledge forward)

3. . . . . . . .sist (remain throughout)

4. . . . . . . .nounce (to announce forward or to say)

5. . . . . . . .pare (make ready before)

EXERCISE C   Use each of the words you made in Exercise B in a separate short sentence. Underline each word you select from Exercise B. (Add 20 points for each correct sentence.)

1. . . . .

2. . . . .

3. . . . .

4. . . . .

5. . . . .

REVIEW EXERCISE   Study the words below and be prepared to write them from dictation. Pay special attention to the sound of the *ea* combination in each word. (Add 10 points for each correct answer.)

1. seal

2. great

3. scream

4. ahead

5. break

6. appeal

7. treaty

8. pleasure

9. disease

10. teach

CHAPTER FIVE

Commas Are for Clarity

Nobody ever talks in a perfectly flat, even voice. Your voice rises and falls in pitch, pauses or stops, and the words come fast or slow. All of these changes help you to convey meaning. In written English, punctuation marks take the place of these voice changes. They make sentences easier to understand and easier to read.

The comma is the most common of all punctuation marks. Like your voice changes in speaking, the comma separates groups of words, telling the readers where to slow their reading down and where to pause. Above all, it helps the readers grasp the meaning of what they have read.

There are a few clear and easy-to-learn rules for deciding when a comma is or is not needed, and all of them have to do with making your meaning clear to your readers. In this chapter, you shall study the rules for using commas correctly and the purposes behind these rules.

LESSON 39

How to Punctuate a Series

A *series* is three or more items (words or word groups) written one after the other.

Use commas to separate the items in a series.

Commas are necessary to show what the items in the series—the words or word groups—really are. Without commas, the series may be as confusing to the readers as this example.

CONFUSING For lunch Mrs. Cohen had *coffee cake sandwiches* and *milk*.

Did Mrs. Cohen have sandwiches made of coffee cake? Did she drink both coffee and milk? Was it cake that she had or coffee cake?

CLEAR For lunch Mrs. Cohen had coffee cake, sandwiches, and milk.

A series may consist of verbs, adjectives, adverbs, or phrases as well as nouns.

VERBS IN SERIES Ellen dawdled, hurried, and finally ran to school.
PHRASES IN SERIES We hunted in the woods, on the hill, and near the brook.

Notice that the conjunction *and* (or *or*) comes between the last two items in a series, usually with a comma before it. If all the items in a series are connected by *and* or *or,* no commas are needed.

EXAMPLE   Apply the paint smoothly **and** evenly **and** steadily.

You also place a comma between two adjectives that precede a noun, unless the adjectives are joined by a conjunction.

CORRECT   a healthy, intelligent boy   a healthy **and** intelligent boy

Never place a comma between an adjective and the word it modifies.

INCORRECT   At the party they served orange, grape, and lemon, drinks.
CORRECT   At the party they served orange, grape, and lemon drinks.

EXERCISE   Insert commas wherever they are missing. Some of the sentences are correct as they stand. (Add 5 points for each correctly marked sentence.)

1. Fishing hunting and skin diving are my favorite sports.
2. They saw three deer a rabbit and two opossums.
3. The sand got in Luisa's eyes in her hair and up her nose.
4. Eugene walked ran and even rode a bike to get here.
5. Photographers reporters and tourists got off the plane.
6. A plague of insects damaged crops lawns and fruit trees.
7. Something flashed and sparkled and darted across the sky.
8. Sky trees and flowers glowed in the evening light.
9. We had a telephone electricity and even hot water in our cabin.
10. This restaurant serves breakfast lunch and dinner.
11. The road was blocked by a jungle of branches vines and weeds.
12. The old man had a long narrow and austere face.
13. Red blue and silver fish flashed in the lagoon.
14. I need pineapple and carrots and bananas for the gelatin salad.
15. Mom eats lunch in a restaurant at a diner or sometimes at her desk.
16. She gave him a warm good-looking jacket for his birthday.
17. Iris wanted to be a lawyer an employment counselor or a teacher.
18. We had to supply our own gas electricity heat and hot water for the apartment.
19. Marita took lessons in ballet tap jazz and acrobatics.
20. Ossie had a tie with a blue green and yellow paisley pattern.

A Compound Sentence Needs a Comma

For the sake of variety, you often join together short sentences that have different subjects with a conjunction—a word such as *and* or *but*. The result is called a compound sentence.

Use a comma before <u>and</u>, <u>but</u>, <u>or</u>, <u>nor</u>, **or** <u>for</u> **when it joins the parts of a compound sentence.**

Always keep in mind that a compound sentence contains two (or more) subjects and that each subject has its own verb. A compound sentence is really two simple sentences joined together.

EXAMPLES   I bought a pair of earrings for Mother**, and** Dad bought her a necklace for her birthday.
Ms. Salkeld decided before lunch to buy a new car**, but** the whole afternoon was taken up by details of the purchase.

Long sentences, like these examples, are hard for the eye to grasp without some kind of help, and you provide that help in the form of commas. When a compound sentence is sufficiently short, a comma is not necessary.

EXAMPLES   <u>Fish swim</u> **and** <u>birds fly</u>.
<u>He liked it</u> **but** <u>I didn't</u>.

EXERCISE A   Supply the necessary commas. Remember that if the two parts of a compound sentence are short, a comma is not needed. (Add 10 points for each correct answer.)

1. Snakes are both legless and armless but plates attached to moveable ribs allow them to swim and crawl.

2. Contrary to legend, a snake's tongue is not forked but a snake does feel and smell with the aid of its tongue.

3. When in danger, a snake covers a hole with its head and its young slip down the hole to safety.

4. Rattlesnakes do not always rattle before striking nor should you expect this warning sign when in the woods.

5. You can determine the age of a tree by the number of rings it has but the number of rattles on a rattlesnake does not tell how old it is.

6. A rattlesnake gains a new rattle each time it sheds its skin but this may occur more than once a year.

7. Sometimes the rattlesnake does not replace the rattles that break off or sometimes two or more rattles grow within a year.

8. Some cobras are capable of forming a hood by expanding the moveable ribs behind the head and this feature makes them easy to identify.

9. The cobra is more aggressive than the rattlesnake and its venom is more powerful.

10. Some countries are free of snakes but the United States is not one of them.

Do not confuse a compound sentence with a simple sentence that has a compound predicate. A compound sentence usually requires a comma before the conjunction. A compound predicate does not.

NONSTANDARD   The storm caused great damage, and washed away several bridges. (This is a simple sentence with a compound predicate. Both verbs have the same subject and should *not* be separated by a comma.)

STANDARD   The storm caused great damage and washed away several bridges.

If a compound predicate contains more than two verbs, the rule for commas in series applies.

STANDARD   The storm damaged houses, blew down trees, and washed away bridges.

EXERCISE B   Insert the missing commas in the following paragraph, including some commas for words or word groups in series. Watch out for compound predicates. (Add 10 points for each correct answer.)

1   The ancient Egyptians worshiped a god called Osiris and they
2   attributed to him the power of life and death. In statues, Osiris usually
3   looks like a man wears a beard and a crown and is wrapped in strips
4   of cloth. His hands stick out from the strips of cloth and carry a
5   shepherd's crook and a whip. Osiris had power over the growth of
6   crops the annual flooding of the Nile and agriculture in general.
7   Worship of Osiris was widespread in the ancient world and it reached
8   Greece Rome and even Spain. Finland Sweden and other countries
9   had similar gods.

Commas for Interrupters

Both in writing and in speaking you often use expressions like *however* and *on the other hand* that are not strictly necessary. Because such expressions break up, or interrupt, a sentence which would be complete without them, they are called *interrupters*. You separate an interrupter from the rest of the sentence with commas. The commas are there to make the sentence easier to read.

Use commas to set off expressions that interrupt the sentence.

EXAMPLE   He went, of course, because he was afraid.

Only one comma is necessary when the interrupter comes at the beginning or end of the sentence.

EXAMPLES   On the other hand, I can hardly blame her.
　　　　　　She might have taken the train, for example.

Here are some of the most common interrupters:

on the contrary	to tell the truth	however	I suppose
generally speaking	in my opinion	naturally	in fact
on the other hand	for example	of course	I think

Some of these expressions are not always used as interrupters.

INTERRUPTER　　　　　She will, I suppose, get angry and go home.

NOT AN INTERRUPTER　　I suppose she will get angry and go home.

A few words like *why, well,* and *yes* are often used to get a sentence started. When used in this way, these are *introductory words.*

Introductory words are set off with commas.

EXAMPLES   Why, who would have believed it?
　　　　　　Well, I'm not convinced.

An *appositive* is a word that means the same thing as the word it follows. It is usually set off with commas. An *appositive phrase* is an appositive with its modifiers.

Appositives and appositive phrases are usually set off with commas.

EXAMPLES   Venus, the evening star, is actually a planet.
　　　　　　Enrico Romaro, the tallest boy in the class, led the singing.

Helen Freeman, <u>the valedictorian and without question the most remarkable person to graduate from this school in years</u>, went to Stanford.

If the appositive is a single word (especially someone's name), it is not necessary to set it off with commas.

EXAMPLES   Fannie brought her dog <u>Butch</u>.

He went to Florida with his brother <u>Art</u>.

EXERCISE A Underline the various kinds of interrupters. Insert commas where needed. (Add 10 points for each correctly marked sentence.)

1. Why I don't know what the world's coming to!

2. In my opinion that person is up to no good.

3. Well don't expect Angie to get here late.

4. Ireland the Emerald Isle lies off the coast of Europe.

5. In fact you'll live to regret it.

6. Just at twilight the finest hour of the day the moon rose.

7. The auditorium was a gift of Henry Allerdyce the financier.

8. His words I believe struck home.

9. Constance Whitman the helicopter pilot promised to be there.

10. I told them on the contrary that my brother Eric was not the man.

EXERCISE B Insert commas wherever necessary. (Add 10 points for each correctly marked sentence.)

1   Edythe White my neighbor wants to act. In my opinion she would
2   make a fine performer. She studies acting with Reynold Williams
3   the famous director at a theater workshop. A theater workshop is
4   of course an acting school connected to a theater. Naturally students
5   can try out for roles in theater performances. Edythe will no doubt
6   audition for one of the roles in a summer production of *The Glass*
7   *Menagerie*. In fact the director told her that she had a good chance
8   of getting a part. Indeed Edythe can sing and dance as well as
9   act. To tell the truth you could say that she comes alive when
10   on stage. Eventually Edythe would like to appear in musical comedies
11   as well as in straight drama plays.

Commas in Dates and Addresses

In a date or an address consisting of two or more parts, put a comma after each part.

DATE   On December 19, 1973, we moved to our present address.
ADDRESS My cousins live at 175 Wood Street, Akron, Ohio 44303.

The parts of a date may include the time of day; the day of the week; the month (with the day of the month); and the year. Except at the end of a sentence, a comma must follow each item in a date made up of any two or more of these parts.

EXAMPLE At 6:00 P.M., Wednesday, November 9, 1977, they returned.

The parts of an address should include the street number and the street; the city; the state and zip code; and the country, if the letter is mailed from outside it.

EXAMPLE 1260 Bowman Street, Brooklyn, New York 11220, U.S.A.

EXERCISE A Punctuate the following addresses and dates as if they were within sentences. (Add 20 points for each correctly punctuated sentence.)

A. a boy from Greenwich, Rhode Island,

1. on Saturday July 28 1754

2. from 631 Chatham Lane Houston Texas 77027

3. at 287 Austin Street Duluth Minnesota 55803

4. since Monday August 13 1968

5. to 25 Foster Lane Billings Montana 59102

EXERCISE B Insert the necessary commas in the following sentences. Three sentences are correct as they stand. (Add 4 points for each correctly marked sentence.)

1. This letter was sent from 18 Grassmere Avenue Flint Michigan 48504.

2. She also visited friends in Dallas and Midland.

3. On October 1 1847 Maria Mitchell discovered a new comet.

4. World War II ended on September 2 1945.

5. Stacy Kempner moved from East Brunswick New Jersey to Boulder Colorado.

6. On June 1 1937 Amelia Earhart started out on her final flight from Miami Florida.

7. My cousin, Mary Lee, lives in Atlanta New Mexico not in Georgia.

8. Abigail Adams died on October 18 1818.

9. Tony's address is 194 Foothill Drive Ogden Utah 84403.

10. The Leonards sailed on Thursday November 7 1974 for a trip to Europe.

11. Darlene used to live at 1002 Carson Avenue Baltimore Maryland 21224.

12. Martin Luther King, Jr., was assassinated on April 4 1968 in Memphis Tennessee.

13. Relatives from Charleston West Virginia are visiting us.

14. We stopped at Houston Texas on our way to Mexico.

15. Room 2930 52 Whitney Way Erie Pennsylvania 16511 is the address given in the letter.

16. Next week we hope to drive to Stockbridge Massachusetts.

17. The wedding took place on Thursday December 28 1967 at 2:00 P.M.

18. Melba has just returned from a trip to Paris France.

19. My home until 1974 was on Michigan Boulevard in Chicago.

20. These pictures were taken last month at Lake George New York.

21. *Old Ironsides* was launched on October 21 1815.

22. Elizabeth Barrett lived at 50 Wimpole Street London England.

23. On September 12 1846 she married Robert Browning.

24. It took Narcissa Whitman four months to travel from Missouri to the Columbia River in 1836.

25. Gwendolyn Brooks was born in 1917 and has lived for most of her life in Chicago Illinois.

Chapter Review

EXERCISE A Insert commas where needed to separate the words or phrases in series. (Add 10 points for each correctly marked sentence.)

1. You will have to take shirts pants socks and shoes.

2. Small yellow shrill birds flew across the field.

3. We had ice cream and cake and candy and pie for dessert, and now we feel sort of funny.

4. On foot in cars by ferry and by train, they fled.

In the following sentences, set off the interrupters by commas.

5. For example you were much too soft at the beginning.

6. I still say however that she should not have gone alone.

7. The nation's economy will we trust improve.

In the following sentences, insert commas where necessary to separate the parts of addresses and dates.

8. During her senior year, her address was East Hall 203 Milnor Avenue Buffalo New York 14218.

9. All records for dates prior to January 23 1907 were destroyed in the fire of November 1919 that burned down City Hall.

10. The building at 17 Lamar Drive Kansas City Missouri is for rent.

EXERCISE B The following paragraph puts to use all the rules about commas studied in this chapter. Insert the commas omitted. (Add 2 points for each correctly placed comma.)

WOULD YOU BELIEVE?

1   You are no doubt used to hearing about basketball centers football

2   ends and baseball pitchers who are more than six feet six inches tall.

3   Indeed the greatest former star of basketball Wilt Chamberlain is more

4   than seven feet tall. Wilt however would look rather small beside

5   either Robert Pershing Wadlow or Albert Johann Kramer. Kramer

6   a giant from the Netherlands is officially listed as eight feet four

7   inches tall but Wadlow attained a height of eight feet eleven. His

greatest recorded weight was 491 pounds but at the time of his death he weighed only 439 pounds. Wadlow the tallest person of all time died on July 15 1940 in Manistee Michigan. Jane Bunford the tallest woman in medical history measured seven feet eleven inches. She was born on July 26 1895 and lived in Birmingham England. Delores Pullard born in De Quincy Louisiana was seven feet tall at the age of seven and at the age of fourteen she was credited with a height of eight feet two inches but medical evidence shows that her true height was seven feet five-and-one-half inches. The tallest living woman Tiliya lives in a village in Bihar State northeastern India and her height is said to be seven feet five inches. Circuses have often claimed giants eight or nine feet tall but these claims do not stand up. Circus giants in fact are usually under contract not to be measured. No circus giant has ever been found to be taller than Wadlow Kramer or Jane Bunford. One circus for example claimed the "World's Tallest Man" of nine feet six inches but he was found to be under seven feet four. Why even respectable scientists get carried away with this game of claims. Until 1872, anthropologists biologists and doctors believed that Daniel Cajanus a Finn was nine feet three-and-a-half inches tall and the greatest giant who ever lived. His bones were dug up and measured in fact two feet less. Ivan Stepanovich Lushkin a member of the Russian Imperial Regiment of Guards lived from 1811 to 1844. He was reported to have attained the height of almost eight feet four inches but modern investigation indicates that his maximum height was in fact only seven feet ten-and-one-quarter inches. It was just a tall tale!

Cumulative Review

A Underline the subjects of each sentence once and the verbs twice. Circle any complements. (Add 4 points for each correct answer.)

1. Batman and Robin raced to the scene of the crime and caught the robber.

2. Miss Diaz brought a macaw back with her from South America.

3. Myron held his breath for a minute, but his parents ignored his tantrum.

4. The bear turned from the trail and ran away through the woods.

5. The mayor spoke vigorously, but public apathy became more widespread.

6. A few people visited the polls.

B In the following paragraph, identify the part of speech of each italicized word by writing the appropriate abbreviation above it: *n.* for noun; *pron.* for pronoun; *adj.* for adjective; *v.* for verb; *adv.* for adverb; and *prep.* for preposition. (Add 4 points for each correct answer.)

1   The *Egyptian* god Osiris was married to Isis. His *brother* Set, how-
2   ever, *envied their* happiness. *One* day, Osiris *was* hunting, and Set *killed*
3   Osiris and cut his body *into fourteen* pieces. He scattered the pieces
4   *far* and wide. Isis, however, found *all* the pieces and put *them together*
5   *again. Through* her power, she brought *Osiris back* to life. She *also*
6   *had* a child named Horus. When he grew up, Horus *battled* Set and
7   killed him. In *this* myth, Osiris' *return* to life represents the *yearly*
8   *rebirth* of the earth in *springtime.*

C The complements in the following paragraph are italicized. Indicate the kind of complement by writing above each the abbreviation *d.o.* (for direct object) or *s.c.* (for subject complement). (Add 10 points for each correct answer.)

1   Staten Island is *one* of the five boroughs of New York City. It
2   received its *name* in 1609 from Henry Hudson. He named *it* after

3   the States General of the Dutch Republic. There was once an old

4   vaudeville *joke* about how the island got its *name*. As the Half Moon

5   sailed into The Narrows, a sailor sighted *land* off the coast of New

6   Jersey. He pointed to it and asked, "Iss dat an *island?*" The Dutch

7   bought the *region* from the American Indians. Unfortunately, the

8   English also purchased the *island.* Actually, Staten Island was bought

9   on six separate occasions. In 1898, it officially became *part* of New

10   York City.

D Put parentheses around all the prepositional phrases in the following paragraphs. Above each phrase, write the abbreviation *adj.* if it is an adjective phrase or *adv.* if it is an adverb phrase. (Add 2 points for each correct answer.)

THE BEGINNINGS OF FRANCE

1   The great empire of the Romans was declining. The great roads

2   built by the Romans were destroyed and the aqueducts carried no

3   more water. Gradually, uncivilized tribes from the areas to the east

4   of the Rhine penetrated its borders and settled in areas under Roman

5   rule. The Franks, a tribe from the Main Valley, moved into the lands

6   between the Rhine and the Somme and occupied Belgium and

7   northern France. During the decline of Roman strength, the Franks

8   seized power, and by A.D. 500 they ruled most of Gaul. *France,* the

9   modern name for the region then called Gaul, comes from the word

10   *Frank.*

11   A century later, France had broken up into several small kingdoms,

12   but in 719 a Frankish king named Charles Martel seized power and

13   reunited France. Meanwhile, the Arabs had conquered most of the

14   Middle East, northern Africa, and Spain, and now they were threat-

15   ening Europe also. Then in the year A.D. 732 the Arabs actually

16   invaded Europe. In a great battle near Tours, France, the invading

17   Arabs were defeated by Charles Martel. By his exploits, he showed

18   that he was well named indeed, for *Charles Martel* means *Charles*

19   *the Hammer.* He saved Europe from invaders.

Building Vocabulary: Dictionary Meanings

If you had to rely purely on your own experience with words in context, your knowledge of the meanings of many words would be limited indeed. That is why a dictionary is so useful. The meanings which a dictionary gives for a word are a kind of summary of all the different contexts in which the word is used—all the meanings it may have.

The dictionary meanings of a word are based on actual contexts in which the word has been used.

Dictionary makers do not make up word meanings out of their own heads. They collect dozens, sometimes hundreds, of contexts in which a word has been used. They find these examples everywhere—in literature, in newspapers, in speeches, and in government documents. For a word like *competitor,* for example, the contexts might include:

CONTEXTS   The **competitors** in the track meet were evenly matched. A business must keep up with its **competitors**.

By studying and comparing the contexts in which the word is used, dictionary editors are able to write a concise summary of its meaning that will fit every context. This dictionary meaning of a word is its *definition.* For *competitor,* this might be:

DEFINITION   **Competitor**: One who strives for the same goal as another; a rival.

EXERCISE   Study the contexts in which the words below are used. Then, to the left of the number, write the letter of the definition on the next page that fits the contexts in which each word is used. (Add 10 points for each correct answer.)

CONTEXTS

.... 1. **abhor** /ab háur/, *v.:* Truly to love justice a person must also *abhor* injustice. The decent people of the earth *abhor* crimes.

.... 2. **discord** /dís kaurd/, *n:* The two speakers' dislike of one another was a source of *discord* during the discussion.

.... 3. **intricate** /ín tri kit/, *adj.:* The wiring of an electronic computer is extremely *intricate.* The procedure for launching a satellite is an *intricate* one.

.... 4. **banish** /bán ish/, *v.:* Hearing about other people's troubles will often *banish* our own worries.

..... 5. **consistent** /kən sís tənt/, *adj.:* Clement had straight *D*'s on his last report card, but at least he was *consistent*.

..... 6. **hysterical** /his tér i kəl/, *adj.:* A person who laughs or cries for no reason may be *hysterical*.

..... 7. **appalling** /ə páu ling/, *adj.:* Cruelty to children and animals is *appalling* to most of us. The sinking of the *Titanic* was an *appalling* disaster.

..... 8. **eligible** /él ə jə bəl/, *adj.:* The Constitution says that to be *eligible* for the Presidency a person must be at least thirty-five years old and "a natural-born citizen."

..... 9. **plausible** /plaú zə bəl/, *adj.:* Beverly's explanation seemed *plausible* enough until we found out what really happened.

..... 10. **colossal** /kə lós əl/, *adj.:* The building of the Panama Canal was a *colossal* undertaking. The *colossal* height of Mount Everest is awe-inspiring.

DEFINITIONS

a. To dislike intensely, with a feeling of disgust; to shrink from in fear and loathing.
b. Shocking; causing fear and horror with a feeling of helplessness.
c. To put out of a country; to drive from one's thoughts.
d. Huge; gigantic.
e. Keeping to the same principles or kind of behavior.
f. Harsh disagreement between persons; confused, ugly sound.
g. Suitable or qualified for something; fit to be chosen.
h. Emotionally out of control; wild, frantic.
i. Complicated; made up of many small details.
j. Seemingly true but without proof one way or the other.

REVIEW EXERCISE In the space to the left of each sentence, write the letter of the best meaning for the italicized word. (Add 20 points for each correct answer.)

..... 1. "I can't *tolerate* a player who breaks training," said the coach.
   a. dislike   b. put up with   c. be friendly with

..... 2. The judge *speculated* that bad housing is a cause of crime.
   a. theorized   b. insisted   c. believed

..... 3. This device automatically *ejects* the used blade from the razor.
   a. sharpens   b. takes hold of   c. throws out

..... 4. The custom of dueling is now *extinct*.
   a. well known   b. died out   c. illegal

..... 5. The large crowd *hampered* the efforts of the fire fighters.
   a. cheered   b. approved of   c. interfered with

© 1977 HBJ

Spelling: Words Containing the Prefixes mis-, dis-, and un-

If you have to stop after writing the first *s* in the word *misspell*, and wonder whether to use one *s* or two, or debate about whether to use one or two *n*'s in *unnatural*, take heart. You can spell these words and a great many other similar ones by learning to think of such words as being made up of two parts—a base word and a prefix added to the beginning of the base word to change its meaning. Look at the words below to see how this is done:

PREFIX		BASE WORD		NEW WORD
mis	+	understand	=	**mis**understand
mis	+	step	=	**mis**step
dis	+	appear	=	**dis**appear
dis	+	satisfied	=	**dis**satisfied
un	+	usual	=	**un**usual
un	+	numbered	=	**un**numbered

Can you think of a rule to help you spell words containing the prefixes *mis-, dis-,* and *un-?* Here it is:

When adding a prefix that ends with a single consonant to a base word, write the prefix first and then the base word. Do not change the spelling of either.

EXERCISE A   Join each prefix and base word below to make a new word. Write the new word, correctly spelled, in the blank. (Add 10 points for each correct answer.)

	PREFIX		BASE WORD		NEW WORD
1.	mis	+	behave	=	....
2.	dis	+	obey	=	....
3.	un	+	kind	=	....
4.	mis	+	state	=	....
5.	dis	+	similar	=	....
6.	un	+	named	=	....
7.	un	+	needed	=	....

8. mis   +   statement   = ...

9. un   +   noticed   = ...

10. dis   +   please   = ...

EXERCISE B   Make a new and appropriate word by adding the prefix given in parentheses to the italicized word in each sentence below. (Add 20 points for each correct answer.)

1. The third word on your paper is ....*spelled.*   (mis)

2. They were so frightened they were ....*able* to say a word.   (un)

3. The sugar lumps slowly began to ....*solve* in the iced tea.   (dis)

4. That remark of yours was quite ....*necessary.*   (un)

5. His last statement was intentionally ....*leading.*   (mis)

EXERCISE C   Use five of the ten words from Exercise A in separate original sentences. (Add 20 points for each correct answer.)

1. ....

2. ....

3. ....

4. ....

5. ....

REVIEW EXERCISE   Study the words below and be prepared to write them from dictation. Pronounce the prefix in each word carefully and then listen intently to the prefixes when your teacher dictates the words. (Add 5 points for each correct answer.)

1. precaution	11. promotion
2. perfect	12. prepare
3. prearrange	13. professor
4. propeller	14. persuade
5. persist	15. percolate
6. precedes	16. pronounce
7. prolong	17. provide
8. permanent	18. precise
9. predict	19. proposal
10. perforate	20. perfume

SUBJECT AND VERB In the following paragraph, underline the subject of each sentence once and the verb twice (including helping verbs). Then, in the space after each sentence, show what *kind* of sentence it is according to the following code. (Add 5 points for each correctly marked sentence.)

    a—simple sentence with one subject and one verb
    b—simple sentence with compound subject
    c—simple sentence with compound verb
    d—simple sentence with compound subject and compound verb
    e—compound sentence

1. Nero was emperor of Rome in the early Christian era. (. . . .) 2. He loved extravagant banquets and huge parties. (. . . .) 3. Because of the tax revenues of the empire, he was rich, and he indulged his taste for extremes of luxury. (. . . .) 4. No one could oppose him. (. . . .) 5. Conservative noblemen and public-spirited citizens of every class condemned the wastefulness of Nero's parties but hid their feelings for fear of Nero. (. . . .) 6. Suddenly a fire broke out in Rome. (. . . .) 7. It began in a shopping district and was spread by the wind. (. . . .) 8. Ancient Rome had little fire-fighting equipment, and the fire spread rapidly. (. . . .) 9. First it burned all the low-lying sections of the city and then spread to the hills. (. . . .) 10. Palaces, temples, public buildings, tenements, and shops all burned to the ground. (. . . .) 11. Nero seemed indifferent to the destruction. (. . . .) 12. According to one historian, some Romans actually encouraged the fire and openly spread it. (. . . .) 13. Others hindered the fire fighters. (. . . .) 14. These men may have been in Nero's pay. (. . . .) 15. Nero's own palace burned, but his many enemies blamed him for the fire. (. . . .) 16. According to them, he appeared on a private stage during the fire and sang a song about the fire. (. . . .) 17. Nero fiddled and Rome burned. (. . . .) 18. Afterward, Nero organized a persecution of the Christians and blamed them for the fire. (. . . .) 19. He had no evidence. (. . . .) 20. Eventually, the senate proclaimed Nero a public enemy, and he committed suicide. (. . . .)

PARTS OF SPEECH Identify the part of speech of each italicized word. Above the word write one of the following abbreviations: *n.* for noun; *pron.* for pronoun; *adj.* for adjective; *v.* for verb; *adv.* for adverb; and *prep.* for preposition. (Add 4 points for each correct answer.)

1   The *nursery* stories and nursery *rhymes* called "Mother Goose
2   stories" *have* a *long history,* and *their* origin in many cases cannot
3   *be* traced. Some of *them first appeared* in *book* form in a *book* printed
4   in *Venice* in 1550. *During* the *seventeenth* century in *France* the stories
5   were *already* known as "Mother Goose stories," and *early* in the
6   eighteenth century, *one* of the *French* books was translated *into*
7   *English. Later* an Englishman *published* a collection of *rhymes* called
8   Mother Goose's Melody.

THE SENTENCE BASE Indicate the sentence base in each of the following sentences. Underline the subject of each sentence once and the verb twice (including helping verbs). Circle the complement and above it write *d.o.* for a direct object and *s.c.* for a subject complement. Some sentences are compound or have compound parts but not every sentence has a complement. Remember that a subject complement follows a linking verb while a direct object comes only after an action verb. (Add 5 points for each correctly marked sentence.)

1. Many similarities exist between the cultures of the ancient Egyptians and the cultures of the Aztecs and Incas of Central America.
2. Perhaps parts of the Americas were visited by ancient Egyptians.
3. This was the belief of the Norwegian scientist Thor Heyerdahl.
4. He thoroughly researched ancient Egyptian culture and gathered information from prehistoric tombs.
5. He copied blueprints for ship construction from inscriptions on these tombs.
6. A boat from that period would have been built out of papyrus.
7. Papyrus is an ancient, paperlike material, and the Egyptians had a special process for its manufacture.
8. The construction of a boat with ancient Egyptian materials and methods seemed possible.
9. They completed the boat and named it *Ra* after the sun god of Egypt.

10. These adventurers stored no meat on the ship, and all milk products were left behind.

11. The sailors would eat an ancient diet of dates, nuts, and raisins.

12. Heyerdahl and his crew left Africa in the *Ra,* in 1969, but, after two months at sea, the boat was destroyed.

13. These courageous adventurers were not discouraged.

14. They rebuilt their ship and followed the same course in 1970.

15. This time they took two mascots, a duck and a monkey, and these animals were the main source of entertainment on the boat.

16. After 57 days, the *Ra II* completed its journey of 3,200 miles.

17. You may have read of one of Heyerdahl's earlier adventures.

18. In 1947, he built the raft *Kon Tiki* and sailed the Pacific.

19. Perhaps South American natives had traveled in this manner to the islands in the South Pacific.

20. Certainly Heyerdahl demonstrated its possibility.

THE PREPOSITIONAL PHRASE Put parentheses [( )] around the prepositional phrases in the following paragraph. Decide whether each phrase modifies a noun or pronoun (an *adjective* phrase) or a verb (an *adverb* phrase). Write the abbreviation *adj.* above each adjective phrase and *adv.* above each adverb phrase. (Add 2 points for each correct answer.)

1 Anne was traveling in Europe with her parents for the summer.
2 They stayed in France during the month of August. Anne had
3 learned before coming to Europe that in France everyone used metric
4 weights and measures. The metric system is based on powers of ten.
5 Multiplication or division by ten would give you a larger or smaller
6 unit of measure. Length is measured in meters. One thousand meters
7 is called one kilometer. The prefix *kilo* means one thousand (10^3).
8 Anne's parents taught her a rule of thumb about the metric system.
9 One kilogram roughly equals two pounds, one liter is slightly more
10 than one quart, and one kilometer is somewhat more than one half
11 of a mile. This rule can be used for most situations except those where
12 precise measurement is required. Anne found it useful throughout

13   her stay in Europe. In all the stores, milk was sold by the liter and
14   potatoes by the kilogram.

15   On August 17, all of the family went to a bike race held outside
16   town. The course for the race was twenty kilometers. The course ran
17   over a flat paved track through the woods. Anne knew that a twenty
18   kilometer course roughly equaled ten miles but she wanted a more
19   precise figure for the length of the course in miles. In the dictionary,
20   she found that one kilometer equals .621 miles. By multiplying, she
21   discovered that the race course equaled 12.42 miles.

22   Anne waited with her parents at the starting line. They had brought
23   chairs and placed them beneath the trees. After the starting shot,
24   they drove in their car to the finish line. The winner of the race
25   reached the finish line before them. This cyclist had traveled the
26   course in fourteen minutes at a speed of approximately 86 kilo-
27   meters per hour or about 53 miles per hour. This speed did not break
28   the record for this event. The crowd gathered around the winner and
29   cheered. Anne decided that she would train during the year and
30   compete next summer.

PUNCTUATION Add the commas that are missing from the following
paragraph. (Add 5 points for each correct answer.)

1   In these days of jet planes space travel and satellites, we do not
2   always remember the recent development of flight. Yet the age of
3   flight is in fact a very new chapter in our history and we are still
4   even today only at the beginning of it. Actually some people can
5   still remember the Wright brothers' first flight at Kittyhawk North
6   Carolina on December 17 1903. Within a few years, flight across the
7   Atlantic became possible and on May 20 1927 Colonel Charles A.
8   Lindbergh one of the first American mail pilots began his solo flight.
9   He set out from Roosevelt Field and reached Le Bourget Airport
10   Paris France the following day May 21.

CHAPTER SIX

A *run-on sentence* is a little *more* than a complete sentence while a *sentence fragment* is a little *less.* Both are serious errors which interfere with the writing of clear, effective sentences. Even though you may know perfectly well just what a sentence is, there are certain situations in which it is quite easy to fall into the trap of writing something that is *less* than a complete sentence (a sentence fragment) or *more* than a complete sentence (a run-on sentence). By learning to recognize these situations, as you shall in this chapter, you can also learn to avoid both of these sentence errors.

LESSON 47

Spotting Sentence Fragments

A <u>sentence fragment</u> is a separated part of a sentence that does not express a complete thought.

A part of a sentence may become so important to the writer that it comes unstuck from the sentence with which it belongs. The result is a sentence fragment. Suppose, for example, that you saw a famous tennis player who had her picture in all the papers. This would be exciting and important. It might therefore seem sensible to write:

EXAMPLE   Yesterday, I saw Rosemary Casals. *A famous tennis player.*

But *what* about *a famous tennis player?* As this group of words is written, the reader cannot be sure whether it belongs with the preceding sentence or introduces a new idea. Notice that while *player* might be the subject of a new sentence, this group of words by itself does not tell us anything about the tennis player because it does not have a verb. The confusion can be cleared up very easily, however, simply by tacking the word group back onto the preceding sentence. Then it is seen at once that it serves to identify *Rosemary Casals*—she is the famous tennis player.

EXAMPLE   Yesterday, I saw <u>Rosemary Casals</u>, <u>a famous tennis player.</u>

Notice how the following fragments are corrected by the addition of the missing sentence parts.

97

FRAGMENT	The boat on the river.
SENTENCE	**The boat on the river** was heading for a collision.
FRAGMENT	Drinking a cup of coffee.
SENTENCE	A man was sitting at the counter **drinking a cup of coffee**.

In each case, a verb or a subject, or both, must be added before the word group can be part of a complete sentence. A complete sentence needs both a subject and a verb.

EXERCISE A All of the following word groups are *written* as sentences, but some are actually sentence fragments rather than sentences. Indicate which is which by writing *S* (for sentence) or *F* (for fragment) in the space at the left. Remember that a complete sentence must have both a subject and a verb. (Add 10 points for each correct answer.)

.... 1. At the foot of the tallest mountain.

.... 2. The lights were visible at the foot of the tallest mountain.

.... 3. There we saw three blackbirds sitting on a fence.

.... 4. Three blackbirds sitting on a fence.

.... 5. A quarterback famous for his ability on offense.

.... 6. The flag flapping gently in the morning breeze.

.... 7. Even for all the tea in China I wouldn't do it.

.... 8. Breakfast cereal without cream or sugar.

.... 9. The author of at least three best-selling novels, all published in at least four languages on three continents.

.... 10. It was Margaret O'Reilly herself.

EXERCISE B In the space provided, rewrite each of the following sentence fragments, adding whatever words are necessary in order to make a complete sentence. (Add 20 points for each correct sentence.)

1. Before the end of the program.

. . . .

2. The chair next to the fireplace.

. . . .

3. But never came back again.

. . . .

4. Asked about her ambitions.

. . . .

5. Not the patient in the bed by the window.

. . . .

Phrase Fragments

Two kinds of phrases are often written as fragments: the prepositional phrase and the appositive phrase. The temptation to write these phrases as if they were complete sentences is especially great when they come near the end of a sentence and contain several modifiers. Remember, however, that sentence completeness has nothing to do with length. Even a very short group of words like *someone laughed* can be a perfectly good complete sentence provided (1) it has a subject and a verb, and (2) it expresses a complete thought.

The Prepositional Phrase A prepositional phrase is a phrase that begins with a preposition and ends with a noun or pronoun. The noun or pronoun may have modifiers, and several prepositional phrases may be strung together, one after the other. When a prepositional phrase acts as an adjective or adverb (as it almost always does), it must be connected as closely as possible with the word it modifies. It should *not* be cut off as a sentence fragment.

FRAGMENT We had excellent seats./ *On the fifty-yard line.* (*On the fifty-yard line* is an adjective phrase modifying *seats.*)

ATTACHED We had excellent seats on the fifty-yard line.

FRAGMENT The Smyths finally sold their farm./ *To an energetic Texan.* (*To an energetic Texan* is an adverb phrase modifying *sold.*)

ATTACHED The Smyths finally sold their farm to an energetic Texan.

The Appositive Phrase An appositive is a word that means the same as the word it follows and explains it in some way. An appositive and its modifiers make up an *appositive phrase.* An appositive phrase should always be closely connected with the word it explains, not cut off as a sentence fragment.

FRAGMENT We read a book about Madame Curie./ *The scientist who discovered radium and polonium.* (*Scientist,* with the other italicized words, is an appositive phrase explaining who Madame Curie was.)

ATTACHED We read a book about Madame Curie, the scientist who discovered radium and polonium.

EXERCISE Each numbered item contains two word groups. If both word groups are complete sentences, write *S* for sentence in the blank at the left. If one of the word groups is a fragment, write *F* for fragment and correct the fragment; cross out the period and the incorrect capital letter and write a small letter above it. Put a comma before an appositive. (Add 10 points for each correctly marked sentence.)

F.   A.   On my birthday, we went to the Riverview,ᵃ A large amusement park.

....   1.   Every year, the United States imports millions of bananas from Latin America. The world's leading banana producer.

....   2.   For five years she was not heard from. She was lost in the jungle.

....   3.   In the middle of the night, Alfredo was suddenly awakened. By a curious humming noise outside his window.

....   4.   To some, he seemed merely mistaken. To others, he appeared actually dishonest.

....   5.   At that time, he was still recognized as the heavyweight champion of the world. In every state except New York and Massachusetts.

....   6.   With a glance at the referee and the people in the grandstands on both sides of the field. The captain signaled time out.

....   7.   The next speaker was Dr. Widdicomb. An unusually youthful and robust woman in spite of her advanced age.

....   8.   The bill will probably be defeated. Even after all our efforts.

....   9.   My sister is learning lacrosse. An American Indian game.

....   10.   For Christmas they sent us a box of candied dates. From a fruit farm near their home in California.

Other Phrase Problems

Careless writers often fall into the sentence fragment trap because of phrases built around the verb form ending in *–ing*. If you can see why this happens, you can avoid this sentence error.

By adding the *–ing* ending to the verb stem, you can change almost any verb into a word that does the work of an adjective.

EXAMPLES   laughing children   a hurrying man   the approaching storm

While such *–ing* words are used as adjectives, they still behave like verbs in some respects. In particular, they can have complements, and they can be modified by one-word adverbs and by adverb phrases.

EXAMPLES   children laughing loudly (adverb)

a man hurrying down the street (adverb phrase)

the storm approaching the town (object)

Such *–ing* phrases are often written as sentence fragments. The reason is that with modifiers and complements added, they begin to look like sentences. But since it does not have a subject and a complete verb, an *–ing* phrase cannot be a sentence.

FRAGMENT   Last night, near our house, we saw a man. *Hurrying down the street.*

ATTACHED   Last night, near our house, we saw a man hurrying down the street.

There is another way of correcting this kind of sentence error. If the *–ing* phrase seems especially important, you can change it into a complete sentence by adding a subject and a helping verb.

SENTENCE   Last night, near our house, we saw a man. He was hurrying down the street.

EXERCISE A   Underline the *–ing* words that are used as adjectives in the following sentences, together with any complements or modifiers that are part of the *–ing* phrase. Then draw an arrow from the *–ing* word to the noun or pronoun it modifies. Do *not* underline an *–ing* word that is used with a helping verb as the verb of a sentence. (Add 10 points for each correct sentence.)

A. Gunning his engine, the police officer pulled away from the light.

1. He buried himself in his newspaper, ignoring his problems.

2. Laying aside her notes, the speaker improvised her lecture.

3. Yesterday we were refinishing our picnic table.

4. She watched the windows of the bus anxiously, hoping to see her friend.

5. Teresa was hoping to visit us, but she could not get away.

6. Ossie came down the ladder, carrying his pail of paint.

7. Falling against the step, he cut his leg rather badly.

8. Telling everyone loudly about the injustice of it all, Jon delayed the meeting for an entire hour.

9. Belinda at last found the rake and was happily raking up leaves and burning them in bonfires for the rest of the afternoon.

10. All of the letters lying there in the basket are for the mail carrier.

EXERCISE B   The paragraph below contains all the kinds of phrase fragments that we have studied so far. Correct each fragment by joining it to the sentence with which it belongs. Cross out the incorrect periods. Cross out incorrect capital letters and insert small letters above. (Add 10 points for each correct answer.)

1   Athens was named for Pallas Athena. The goddess of wisdom. The
2   Athenians built a temple to her called the Parthenon. Meaning the
3   temple of the maiden. Some stories say that Athena was the daughter
4   of Zeus. She was born. By springing full-grown from his head.
5   According to other stories. She was the daughter of Poseidon but
6   had disowned him and had asked Zeus to adopt her. Other tales say
7   that she had no father. She entered the world by rising. Out of
8   Mother-Earth. Athena was known as the protector. Of civilized life.
9   She invented the bridle and tamed horses. For people's use. This
10 goddess invented the flute and the trumpet and excelled in all the
11 arts. Except singing. Her skill in weaving and spinning was well
12 known. Athens' fate was said to be tied to Athena's fate. Succeeding
13 when she succeeded and failing when she failed. Her attendant bird
14 was the owl. It still can be seen and heard. Hooting among the ruins
15 of the Parthenon.

What Makes a Sentence Complete?

In writing, you begin a sentence with a capital letter and end with a period, a question mark, or an exclamation point. The capital letter and the end mark of punctuation are signals to the reader that what comes between them is a complete sentence. When you make the mistake of using these signals with a group of words that do not make a complete sentence, the result is a sentence fragment.

A complete sentence expresses a complete thought and makes sense by itself. A subject names what the sentence is about. A predicate says something about the subject. An *in*complete sentence, on the other hand —a sentence fragment—does not express a complete thought and does not make sense by itself. It leaves the reader with an unanswered question. If a group of words leaves you hanging in some way, the chances are that it is a sentence fragment; it needs additional words to complete it.

EXAMPLES *After* Haley threw the main switch. (What happened then? This is a sentence fragment.)
If you don't remember to buy the cheese. (What will happen if you don't remember? This group of words does not say what will happen. It is a sentence fragment.)

Words like *after, although, because, if, since, unless, when,* and *while* often lead writers into the sentence fragment trap. Word groups that begin with these words do not express complete thoughts and do not make sense by themselves. They raise questions that can only be answered if they are part of complete sentences.

EXAMPLES The lights went out <u>after Haley threw the main switch</u>. (This is now part of a complete sentence.)
<u>If you don't remember to buy the cheese</u>, you can't make any ham and cheese sandwiches.

EXERCISE To the left of each numbered item write *S* if it is a complete sentence and *F* if it is a sentence fragment. (Add 10 points for each correct answer.)

.... 1. Because Evelyn had been frightened by a bear near camp.

.... 2. Because she was not tall enough, Kelley dropped basketball.

.... 3. Candace found the trail when she got to the mouth of the canyon.

.... 4. Where neither of us had ever been before.

.... 5. While Cynthia was wandering around in the dark.

.... 6. While he was at camp last summer, Jerome passed lifesaving.

.... 7. Although an old boot and a can of beans were found in the cave.

.... 8. Since no one had lived there for many years.

.... 9. Unless you can pass the swimming test before the end of the summer.

.... 10. Don't take a canoe out unless you can swim.

REVIEW EXERCISE The following paragraph contains sentence fragments of all of the kinds you have studied so far in this chapter. Correct each fragment by crossing out the period and inserting a comma if it is needed. Cross out the incorrect capital letter and write a small letter above it. (Add 10 points for each correctly marked sentence.)

IN AND OUT OF BUSINESS

1 One day when Mari and I were cleaning and greasing our bikes.
2 I had the bright idea of setting up a business of our own. A bicycle
3 repair business. We would make some money. Putting our skill to
4 work for others less energetic and ambitious than we were. Our
5 business venture was organized. Within a week. We set up our repair
6 shop in a shed. Behind the garage at our house. We found out how
7 to order our supplies from the Trident Supply Company. A wholesale
8 bicycle parts dealer in Chicago. We had to work out retail prices
9 for the parts ourselves. Since we bought them at wholesale prices.
10 Our business grew rapidly during the winter. More and more cus-
11 tomers came to us. Because of our good service and low prices. Then
12 suddenly our parents made us drop the whole thing. We were making
13 too much money. Their income-tax deductions for us would be
14 disallowed. If we made any more money. Reluctantly, we went out
15 of the bicycle repair business. We certainly would have continued.
16 Except for the income-tax regulations. Still, we had learned a lot
17 and had fun doing it.

Avoiding Run-on Sentences

A complete sentence presents a single basic idea. The end mark and the capital letter that signal the end of one sentence and the beginning of a new sentence show the reader where one idea ends and a new one begins. A sentence fragment is confusing because it gives the reader only part of an idea. A run-on sentence is confusing in a different way. By running together two or more complete sentences, it gives the reader no help in deciding where one idea ends and a new one begins.

EXAMPLES Claudine ate roast beef her dog ate hamburger.
What can the purpose of his visit have been, it puzzles me.

A run-on sentence consists of two or more sentences separated by only a comma or not separated at all.

The simplest way to correct the run-on sentences in the examples above is to put in two end marks—a period in the first example, a question mark in the second. (The first word in each sentence is then capitalized, of course.)

EXAMPLES Claudine ate roast beef. Her dog ate hamburger.
What can the purpose of his visit have been? It puzzles me.

There is another way of correcting a run-on sentence when the parts are statements (sentences that end with a period). The run-on sentence can be changed into a compound sentence.

EXAMPLE Claudine ate roast beef, but her dog ate hamburger.

Remember, however, that two sentences should only be combined in a compound sentence when the ideas they present are closely related in some way.

EXERCISE A Some of the following sentences are correct as they stand, but others are run-on sentences. In the space at the left, write *S* for each correct sentence and *R* for each run-on sentence. Correct the run-on sentences by crossing out the small letter and putting in a suitable end mark and a capital letter where they belong. (Add 20 points for each correctly marked item.)

.... 1. It worries me to see you go without a coat you could easily catch cold.

.... 2. Why do you suppose leaves change color in the fall it certainly does make the countryside pretty.

.... 3. How beautiful that hillside is when the aspen have all turned yellow, they look like gold in the sun.

.... 4. Just because the train was two hours late, you have no excuse for losing your temper that way.

.... 5. The Japanese lanterns swayed gently in the breeze, casting a delicate yellow light on the porch and on the buffet.

EXERCISE B Correct the run-on sentences in this paragraph. Watch out for sentences that are compound or have compound parts. (Add 10 points for each correct answer.)

1   Michele and Daisy wanted to use their spare time constructively
2   Michele had a beautiful singing voice and Daisy played guitar well.
3   They thought they might entertain hospitalized children on weekends
4   it would give them experience and allow them to put their talents
5   to use. They contacted two local hospitals and found they could work
6   as volunteers their help would be appreciated. Several of their friends
7   became interested in the project it was decided they would form a
8   small troupe. Michele and Daisy would perform folk songs, Catherine
9   would do acrobatic stunts, and Theresa and Judy would perform
10   magic tricks surely the show would be a success. The girls rehearsed
11   for two weeks before the first show they were all somewhat nervous.
12   The hospital officials thought that after lunch on Saturday would be
13   a good time for the show the children's recreation room was set aside
14   for the occasion. Not too many props were needed Michele's parents
15   loaded the props in the car on Saturday morning and brought them
16   to the hospital. There were about seventy-five children in the audi-
17   ence several doctors and nurses were also there. Everyone applauded
18   loudly at the end of the show and the hospital asked the troupe to
19   come back next week the show was a huge success.

Chapter Review

EXERCISE A In the space to the left of each item, write *S* if it is a complete sentence, or *F* if it is a fragment. (Add 10 points for each correct answer.)

.... 1. Collecting antiques can be both fun and profitable.

.... 2. For the sake of starting a collection.

.... 3. Merely because a piece appeals to you.

.... 4. Often antiques increase in value with age.

.... 5. A special piece of delicate design.

.... 6. Fun exploring the history of special items.

.... 7. A pot belly stove from the 1890's is still in good condition.

.... 8. Sitting around the stove on cold December evenings and imagining previous owners.

.... 9. Home-made toys from the turn of the century.

.... 10. We found that going to antique shows makes history more vivid.

EXERCISE B In the space to the left of each item, write *S* if it is a single, complete sentence or *R* if it consists of two or more run-on sentences. Correct the run-on sentences by adding the proper end marks and the missing capital letters. (Add 10 points for each correct answer.)

.... 1. Did you ever read about bees how amazing they are!

.... 2. They are not merely interesting, they are also useful.

.... 3. Bees carry pollen from one flower to another.

.... 4. Some farmers rent hives from professional beekeepers during the blossoming season, their crops are larger as a result.

.... 5. How many different kinds of bees there are they must number in the thousands.

.... 6. We usually think only of the honeybees and bumblebees, occasionally we see a wasp also.

.... 7. Everyone knows what happens when a bee becomes angry, it is the bee's method of protecting itself.

.... 8. Bumblebees are important because with their long tongues they get down into deep flowers.

.... 9. Did you know this fact the bee is very systematic, it finds all of the flowers of one kind and then flies to another kind.

.... 10. Are there any books in our library about bees, I want to read more about them bees are very interesting.

EXERCISE C   This paragraph contains both sentence fragments and run-on sentences. Correct the errors by adding or crossing out periods and capital letters as necessary. (Add 10 points for each correct sentence division.)

DOLLARS AND SCENTS

1   The skunk is a well-known member. Of the weasel family. It is
2   found throughout most of North America. Often living in a hollow
3   tree or a burrow. It is nocturnal, usually seeking its food at night.
4   But also being seen or smelled sometimes during the day. The skunk
5   is famous. For a certain peculiar habit, it can squirt a fluid with a
6   very disagreeable odor. A very effective means of defense. It some-
7   times sends the fluid a distance of ten or twelve feet, but the strong
8   odor travels for miles. As a result, other animals usually stay away
9   from skunks. Skunks eat frogs, gophers, reptiles, and squirrels. They
10 help the farmer. By eating insects and field mice. Sometimes the
11 skunk also raids the henhouses. An important source of profit to the
12 farmer. Because of the skunks' odor and their eating habits, nobody
13 really likes them. Except the farmers who raise skunks for their fur.
14 Skunk fur is widely used in fur coats. The body of the skunk also
15 yields an oil. Of use in the manufacture of liniment.

Cumulative Review

A In the space to the left of each sentence, write *T* if the statement is true and *F* if it is false. (Add 10 points for each correct answer.)

.... 1. A noun is a word that expresses action.

.... 2. A pronoun is never the object of a preposition.

.... 3. Some adverbs answer the question *how often*.

.... 4. An adjective may modify an adverb.

.... 5. A verb is a word that names a person, place, thing, or idea.

.... 6. An adjective may be used as a subject complement.

.... 7. A prepositional phrase consists of a preposition and its object.

.... 8. The same word is sometimes used as an adjective and an adverb without any change in spelling.

.... 9. *Good* is never used as an adverb.

.... 10. Prepositions sometimes modify verbs.

B Underline the subject of each sentence once and the verb twice (including helping verbs). Identify each italicized word by writing above it one of these abbreviations: *d.o.* for direct object; *s.c.* for subject complement; or *o.p.* for object of a preposition. (Add 10 points for each correctly marked sentence.)

1. Spiders are perhaps the most *unpopular* of all insects.

2. Some of the most famous spiders are indeed very *poisonous*.

3. Everyone has heard far too *much* about the famous black widow.

4. On the other hand, very few have actually seen a *black widow*.

5. The black widow is *common* in the South and Southwest.

6. Most of the common spiders are *harmless*.

7. Even harmless spiders, however, can inflict a nasty *bite*.

8. One of the most frightening spiders is the *tarantula*.

9. A full-grown tarantula has a leg-spread of five *inches*.

10. Its bite is not nearly as *dangerous* as generally believed.

C The following sentences contain prepositional phrases and appositive phrases. Put parentheses around each phrase; insert commas where necessary. Draw an arrow from the phrase to the word it modifies or means the same thing as. Then, in the blank at the left, indicate whether the phrase is appositive (*app.*) or prepositional (*prep.*). (Add 10 points for each correctly marked sentence.)

.... 1. Some inventors make a great deal of money.

.... 2. The invention may be only a gadget for everyday use.

.... 3. The inventor then obtains a patent on the new invention.

.... 4. The patent a government document protects the inventor's rights.

.... 5. Margaret E. Knight one of the first women to receive an American patent invented mechanisms concerned with heavy machinery.

.... 6. Many a millionaire's wealth has come from oil.

.... 7. Some Texas farmers sell the mineral rights on their land.

.... 8. Drilling a costly process can ruin even a wealthy person.

.... 9. Some people make fortunes through wise speculations.

.... 10. Elizabeth Arden a financial genius made a fortune in the cosmetics industry.

D In the following paragraph, some commas are missing and others should be removed. Correct the punctuation as necessary. (Add 5 points for each correct answer.)

1 Bernard Baruch financier industrialist economist and statesman
2 was born in Camden South Carolina, on August 19 1870. Graduating
3 from the College of the City, of New York in 1889, Baruch became
4 a member of the Stock Exchange, and pursued a career in finance.
5 He made a fortune at an early age and then he turned his attention
6 to the finances of the government. He was an advisor to Presidents
7 Wilson Roosevelt Truman Eisenhower and Kennedy. Some historians
8 hold that Baruch an advisor to five presidents exerted a greater
9 influence on American government than any other person who did
10 not hold a major political office. He gave a large portion of his private
11 fortune to educational institutions. In fact a school now bears his
12 name. The Bernard M. Baruch, College is located at 17 Lexington
13 Avenue New York New York 10010.

Building Vocabulary: Explaining What Words Mean

There are a good many situations in which you must explain the meaning of words. Perhaps you use a term which your readers or listeners do not know. Or you use a word that has more than one meaning (and many words do). If you are trying to be very clear, you must often explain which meaning you intend. Most important, perhaps, explaining a word's meaning helps you to understand the word and use it accurately.

When you explain what a word means, you are *defining* the word. The definition may be one word or it may be several. To be of any use, all the words in a definition must be understood by the readers or listeners. The definition must also explain the word as it is used *in context*.

An accurate definition of a word can usually be substituted for it in a sentence.

Suppose you read this sentence in a book about ancient history:

EXAMPLE   At the Battle of Cannae in 216 B.C., Hannibal **annihilated** the Roman army under Varro.

The context gives you some help with the meaning of *annihilate*. In a dictionary you may find a definition like this: "to reduce to nothing; to destroy completely." Does the definition fit the context? You try it out in the original sentence to see.

EXAMPLE   At the Battle of Cannae in 216 B.C., Hannibal **destroyed completely** the Roman army under Varro.

Study the following definitions. Try to think of sentences in which each word could be used. Check your sentences by substituting the definition for the word defined.

altercation /ául tər ká shən/, *n.* An angry, quarrelsome argument.

annihilate /ə nī́ ə lāt/, *v.* To destroy completely.

anonymous /ə nón ə məs/, *adj.* Written or done by a person whose name is unknown or concealed.

appropriate /ə prṓ prē it/, *adj.* Suitable; fitting.

ascertain /ás ər tā́n/, *v.* To find out with certainty; to make sure of.

aspiration /ás pə rā́ shən/, *n.* Ambition; a strong desire for honor or advancement.

compute /kəm py-ū́t/, *v.* To work out by arithmetic; to figure.

exclude /iks klū́d/, *v.* To keep a person or thing out of something.

renounce /ri noúns/, *v.* To give up or deny something, especially an idea, by a formal decision and statement.

superfluous /sū̄ pə́r flū əs/, *adj.* Over and above what is needed; unnecessary.

EXERCISE   In each blank, write the word from this lesson that best fits the context. Check your answers by substituting for the word the definition given above. (Add 10 points for each correct answer.)

1. When Lucy Stone, the feminist, graduated from Oberlin College in 1847, she . . . . the opportunity to write the commencement address because she would have had to let a man deliver it.

2. Another book would be . . . ., Rosalie felt, since she had already borrowed more than she could read this month.

3. Blue jeans and a sweat shirt are . . . . clothes for a picnic but not for a formal party.

4. All knowledge of the . . . . author of the old ballad "Sir Patrick Spens" is lost in the mists of time.

5. It does not take an electronic brain to . . . . the difference between having too little money and having enough.

6. "I must . . . . the truth of your charge," said the judge, "before I can take any action."

7. A good newspaper tries to . . . . mere opinion from its news columns, which should be completely factual.

8. The . . . . between the two rivals became more and more noisy and finally ended in a fight.

9. Jane Goodall was filled with . . . . to become a successful ethologist.

10. A conqueror may . . . . an entire nation, but its ideas, if they are true, will live on.

REVIEW EXERCISE In the space to the left of each word, write the letter of the best meaning listed at the right. (Add 10 points for each correct answer.)

. . . .	1. satire	a. confused, ugly sound
. . . .	2. turbulent	b. easily set on fire
. . . .	3. inflammable	c. to twist out of shape
. . . .	4. eloquent	d. excited or confused
. . . .	5. monopoly	e. to dislike intensely
. . . .	6. abhor	f. to permit or put up with
. . . .	7. discord	g. complete control over a product
. . . .	8. distort	h. forceful and persuasive
. . . .	9. banish	i. to put out of a country
. . . .	10. tolerate	j. sarcastic wit

Spelling: Adding –ing to Words Ending in Silent e

When you want to write a verb such as *hope* or *blaze* after a helping verb (*am, is, are,* etc.), do you hesitate before writing the final *e*, and wonder whether to keep or drop the *e* before you add the *–ing*?

Look at the pairs of words below and see if you can determine a pattern:

use—using	write—writing
line—lining	care—caring

How do you think *hope* and *blaze* should be spelled when *–ing* is added to them? A very simple rule will help you remember what to do:

Drop the final silent e before adding –ing.

EXCEPTIONS   die—dying
lie—lying   }Change the *ie* to *y* before adding *–ing.*
tie—tying

dye—dyeing
(meaning *color* or }Keep the silent *e* before adding *–ing*
coloring)   to distinguish this word from *dying.*

EXERCISE A   Add *–ing* to each of the following words. Write the new word in the blank. (Add 10 points for each correct answer.)

1. prove. . . . .   6. vie. . . . .

2. explore. . . . .   7. approve. . . . .

3. complete. . . . .   8. scare. . . . .

4. lie. . . . .   9. dye. . . . .

5. promise.   10. hesitate. . . . .

EXERCISE B   Mentally add *–ing* to each word in parentheses below. Then write the new word in the blank. Each new word will modify the italicized word in that sentence. (Add 10 points for each correct answer.)

1. The doctor looked sadly at the . . . . *man.* (die)

2. We listened to the . . . . *announcement.* (excite)

3. We put too much . . . . *powder* in that cake. (bake)

4. The . . . . *bear* was the best act in the circus. (dance)

5. Gilberto has an extremely . . . . *mind.* (inquire)

6. My aunt is now a . . . . *physician.* (practice)

7. Myra looked at the gift with .... *eyes.* (shine)

8. The fabric shrank during the .... *process.* (dye)

9. What a .... *face* you have this morning! (smile)

10. Laura received .... *news* from her teacher. (encourage)

EXERCISE C Choose five verbs (other than those used in this lesson) that end in silent *e*. Write the verbs in the first column below, and then write them with –*ing* added. (Add 10 points for each correct answer.)

VERB	VERB WITH –*ing* ADDED
1.	....
2.	....
3.	....
4.	....
5.	....

REVIEW EXERCISE Study the words below, paying special attention to the spelling of the prefix in each word. Be ready to write the words from dictation. (Add 4 points for each correct answer.)

1. misunderstand

2. unusual

3. misspell

4. disagree

5. unnamed

6. misbehave

7. dissimilar

8. unable

9. misstate

10. unnoticed

11. displease

12. unnecessary

13. dissatisfied

14. unkind

15. misstep

16. disappear

17. unnumbered

18. disobey

19. misleading

20. misstatement

21. unnatural

22. dissolve

23. misplace

24. disapproval

25. unnerve

CHAPTER SEVEN

Understanding Capital Letters

In written English, capital letters are used to signal certain kinds of words and to begin sentences. Like punctuation, capitalization helps the reader to understand what the writer has said. For clear and effective writing, it is just as important to know when to capitalize as it is to know when to use commas and periods.

LESSON 56

Capitals for Proper Nouns

Names (like George or Chicago) are words that refer to particular persons, places, or things. Such words are called *proper nouns*. You capitalize them to show that they apply to one particular person, place, or thing. All the nouns that are not proper nouns are called *common nouns* and are *not* capitalized.

Capitalize the names of persons.

PROPER NOUNS	COMMON NOUNS
Emily Dickinson	poet (any poet)
Hank Aaron	athlete (any athlete)
Mary, Henrietta, and Louise	girls (any girls)
Snoopy	dog (any dog)

People and animals are not the only individuals that have names. The names of particular businesses, government bodies, and other organizations are also proper nouns and must be capitalized.

Capitalize the names of business firms and other organizations.

EXAMPLES Adler Junior High School Radio Corporation of America
University of Wisconsin The Salvation Army

Words like *junior high school, corporation,* and *university* should never be capitalized unless they are used as part of a name, referring to a particular school, company, or university.

EXAMPLES Standard Oil Company   *but* my mother's company
the New Yorker Hotel   *but* at a nearby hotel

115

Do not capitalize the name of a company's product unless it is part of a proper name.

EXAMPLES   The Firestone Tire and Rubber Company
         but   Firestone tires, the tires on our car

EXERCISE A   In the space to the left of each pair, write the letter of the one that is correctly capitalized. (Add 10 points for each correct answer.)

.... 1. (a) Better Business Bureau   (b) Better Business bureau

.... 2. (a) Birdseye peas   (b) Birdseye Peas

.... 3. (a) a famous General   (b) a famous general

.... 4. (a) Harvard University   (b) Harvard university

.... 5. (a) a High School student   (b) a high school student

.... 6. (a) the Pennsylvania railroad   (b) the Pennsylvania Railroad

.... 7. (a) Texaco gasoline   (b) Texaco Gasoline

.... 8. (a) the Ford motor Company   (b) the Ford Motor Company

.... 9. (a) Schwinn bicycles   (b) Schwinn Bicycles

.... 10. (a) the Schubert Theatre   (b) the Schubert theatre

EXERCISE B   Insert the missing capital letters in the following sentences. Cross out any incorrect capital letter and write the correct small letter above it. (Add 5 points for each correct answer.)

A. A Salvation *a*rmy *t*ruck pulled up in front of our house.

1. There is a fine University in our town, but Wilber's brother is set on going to Dartmouth college.

2. Mr. Benson, who is a salesperson for the Williams sporting goods company, likes the Starlight motel better than any Hotel in town.

3. The Lodge's full name is the Benevolent and protective order of Elks.

4. Crystal is a member of the National organization for Women.

5. The book was published by the firm of harcourt Brace Jovanovich, Inc., one of the better-known Publishing Companies.

6. Andrea Clement, a former investigator for the department of Justice, now teaches at Matthew Wood high school.

7. Langston has an account at the first national bank of Chicago.

116   © 1977 HBJ

More Capitals for Proper Nouns

The name of a city, lake, state, country, or any other geographical location is capitalized because it refers to a particular place.

Capitalize the names of particular places and regions.

EXAMPLES Rochester, Minnesota Lake Texoma Long Island
Kruger National Park Snake River Welland Canal
Isthmus of Panama Asia

You do not capitalize compass directions (north, east, south, west), but when directions are used as names of particular regions, they become names and are therefore capitalized.

EXAMPLES Seattle is the largest city in the Northwest.
The wind is from the west. The Franklins live east of town.

Months, days of the week, and holidays are capitalized, and so are the names of special or important events.

Capitalize the names of special events and calendar items.

EXAMPLES The Strawberry Festival in July earned money for our church.
Histories of the Revolutionary War make fascinating reading.
Thanksgiving Day always falls on a Thursday.
The Japanese were defeated at the Battle of Leyte Gulf.

Remember, however, that seasons are *not* capitalized (spring, summer, fall, winter).

EXAMPLE We worked all winter to get the boat ready for the spring.

Capitalize the names of nations, races, and religions.

EXAMPLES Sweden Caucasian Methodist

EXERCISE A Add capitals where they are necessary in the following sentences. When in doubt about whether to capitalize a word or not, decide if it is a proper noun, referring to only one thing, or a common noun. Correct any incorrect capitals. (Add 4 points for each correct answer.)

A. The largest *c*Country in South *a*america is *B*brazil.

1. Fertilizing wisconsin's light soil improved the crops.

2. Their new office building is on third avenue in new york.

3. We went to the Fox Theater to see the movie about india.

4. Our ranch is in brewster county, texas.

5. The soil in Oak creek canyon is exceptionally rich.

6. My great-grandparents came down the Ohio river on a barge.

7. During our trip to canada, we stopped on cape breton island.

8. When you were in australia, did you visit melbourne?

9. Our play is laid in Sherwood forest near nottingham.

10. I like stories about the West in pioneer days.

11. We went through grant's pass, northwest of medford in oregon.

12. The bears in Yellowstone Park are also famous in the east.

EXERCISE B Capitalize any proper nouns mentioned in the paragraph below. (Add 5 points for each correct answer.)

1   People who remember pearl harbor know that it took place on
2   a sunday, but not many know what day of the week iwo jima fell,
3   or when the battle of the bulge took place. Of course, most important
4   battles in modern history lasted for many days. Even naval engage-
5   ments, such as the battle of midway, took several days. In the middle
6   ages, this was not so, and such decisive struggles as the battle of
7   agincourt lasted only a day. The fate of nations was decided in a
8   few hours of fighting between small armies. But we must remember
9   that all england in Elizabethan times had only five million people.
10 The boston tea party during our war of independence involved only
11 a dozen people or so, and the War of Jenkins' ear was the result
12 of an insult to a single person.

Capitals for Proper Adjectives

An adjective formed from a proper noun is called a *proper adjective.* Most proper adjectives are formed from the name of a nation, a race, or a religion, but some are also formed from the names of people.

Capitalize adjectives formed from the names of nations, races, religions, and other proper nouns.

	NATION	RACE	RELIGION	PERSON
PROPER NOUNS	America	Caucasus	Buddhism	Elizabeth
PROPER ADJECTIVES	American	Caucasian	Buddhist	Elizabethan

Notice that many proper adjectives are also used as nouns when they mean an individual, such as *an American, a Chinese,* or *a Catholic.*

A noun used with a proper adjective is not capitalized unless it is itself a proper noun.

NOT	English Silverware	an Irish Setter	a Protestant Church
BUT	English silverware	an Irish setter	a Protestant church (but: the First Baptist Church, the name of a particular church)

Do not capitalize the names of school subjects, except languages and course names followed by a number.

EXAMPLES	mathematics	history	science
	Latin	English	French
	Geometry I	History II	Biology I

Capitalize words that refer to God.

EXAMPLES	God	the Lord

The word *god* is not capitalized when it refers to gods of ancient mythology. The names of particular gods within mythology are, however, capitalized, just as other proper nouns are.

EXAMPLES   Thor, the thunder god
the god of war
Athena, the goddess of wisdom

EXERCISE Correct the capitalization in the following paragraph, adding capital letters where needed and taking out unnecessary capitals. (Add 4 points for each correct answer.)

119

1   The college in our town has several exchange students who have
2   come here on scholarships to study american history, engineering,
3   Education, and other useful subjects. One of the students, who comes
4   from Tunisia, gave a talk in our french II class. He explained that
5   most of the people of tunisia, and of all of the rest of africa North
6   of the Sahara desert, practice the moslem religion. He said that in
7   many Moslem countries, all shops and offices are closed on fridays.
8   However, sunday is a regular workday, and all businesses are open
9   then. The name of the moslem religion is islam. The Moslems
10   worship allah and the major prophet of Islam is mohammed. The
11   city of mecca is considered the spiritual center of Islam. It is the
12   birthplace of Mohammed.

13   Another exchange student came from New delhi, india. She
14   explained to us that one of the major religions in India is buddhism,
15   which is also practiced in parts of china, burma, japan, tibet, and
16   the Southeastern parts of asia. Buddhists believe that all human
17   suffering is caused by desire. The way to achieve happiness is through
18   renouncing desire. All creatures go through a series of reincarnations
19   during which one is born and dies, is born again and dies again,
20   repeatedly, until the soul reaches a state of enlightenment called
21   nirvana. The major prophet of this religion is Gautama buddha.

REVIEW EXERCISE Correct the capitalization in these sentences, which
review all the capitalization rules up to this point. (Add 5 points for each
correct answer.)

1. The package of French Novels came in the mail on monday.

2. Mrs. waybridge is with the United chewing gum company.

3. The battle of vincennes took place farther West than any other engage-
   ment of the revolutionary war.

4. The priest at the catholic Church was born right here in lyme.

5. Anita Welles is famous for her russian Salad Dressing.

6. Aunt Bea's Company is named for neptune, the Roman God of the
   sea.

Capitals for Titles

A title shows a person's job, rank, or position. It is often capitalized.

Capitalize a title when it comes before a person's name

EXAMPLES   Ms. Louisa Abbott   Mayor Leone   Captain Meggs

You do not usually capitalize a title when it follows a person's name or is used without the name. However, a title may be capitalized when it *takes the place* of a person's name (as in direct address), and the word *president* is capitalized when it means the president of a country.

EXAMPLES   Ella Grasso was elected governor of Connecticut.
Alice Whittaker, treasurer of the club, is up for reelection.
"What is your opinion, Senator?" inquired the interviewer.
The President will address the nation tomorrow.

When they are used as titles, words that show family relationships are capitalized like other titles.

EXAMPLES   We took Aunt Helena with us.   (*Aunt* comes before the name.)
I asked Father to take us for a sail.   (*Father* takes the place of the name.)
My mother is in Mexico just now.   (The pronoun *my* shows that *mother* merely states a relationship and is not used as a name or a title.)

Capitalize the first word and all important words in the titles of books, magazines, and newspapers.

Words like *the, a, an, and,* and *of* in a title are not capitalized unless they are the first word in the title. (You may recall that names of companies and historical events are treated in the same way.)

EXAMPLES   *The Light in the Forest*
The Nation That Refused to Starve
Gone with the Wind

The article *the* used before the name of a magazine or newspaper is not considered part of the title and is therefore not capitalized unless it begins a sentence.

EXAMPLES   the *Atlantic Monthly* (magazine)
the *Springfield Daily News* (newspaper)

In printing, the title of a book, magazine, or newspaper is italicized. In handwriting and in typing, underlining takes the place of italics.

EXERCISE A Capitalize the following book, magazine, and newspaper titles as you would if they were used *within* sentences. (Add 10 points for each correct item.)

1. *daughter of the mountains*
2. the *chicago daily news*
3. the *musical quarterly*
4. *the decline and fall of the roman empire*
5. the *san francisco chronicle*
6. *field and stream*
7. the *times literary supplement*
8. *the posthumous papers of the pickwick club*
9. *harriet the spy*
10. *sam patch, the high, wide, and handsome jumper*

EXERCISE B Insert the missing capitals in the following sentences and correct any capital letters that do not follow the rules in this lesson. (Add 4 points for each correct answer.)

1. My mother has just been made President of her company.
2. Indeed, aunt mabel told me she subscribed to *time*.
3. We were all addressed by the president of the Parent-Teachers' association.
4. We were interviewed by a Reporter from the *village voice*.
5. The president likes to get away from Washington on hot days.
6. The singing was led by colonel Graves of the marine corps.
7. When grandmother Newman comes to visit, she always brings presents.
8. I called judge MacIntyre to ask about the potatoes.
9. Shana Alexander was the Editor of *McCall's* before she became a Columnist for *newsweek*.
10. The Captain of the ship, lieutenant Homer Creech, received a personal letter from secretary of the navy Smith.
11. Do you mean, Uncle, that you never read the *Kansas City star?*
12. After dinner, Mother read aloud from Wanda Gág's translation of *Snow White and the seven dwarfs*.
13. Several of my relatives voted for senator Margaret Chase Smith.

122

Chapter Review

EXERCISE A   Supply needed capitals for the names of persons and organizations in these sentences. (Add 4 points for each correct answer.)

1. Has Audrey joined the tuesday literary club?

2. It was Ms. Samuels who was made a vice-president of the Chase manhattan bank.

3. The whole faculty of the Clara Barton high school was there.

4. Striking employees of the whizzy breakfast cereal company met at the metropolitan theater.

5. Truck drivers often stop at the tip top diner.

6. There is a big sale at murphy, carlson and company.

7. A speaker from faust & company lectured at the optimists club.

8. The Nelsons have joined the first Methodist church.

EXERCISE B   Many capitals have been omitted in the following sentences, and others are unnecessary. Supply the missing capital letters and change the incorrect ones. (Add 2 points for each correct answer.)

1. The battle of gettysburg continued through the fourth of July, 1863, and vicksburg fell on the same day.

2. Both uncle roy and my Father were members of the nineteenth infantry division during the korean war.

3. My aunt was a nurse in north africa, but she met few mohammedans. Her patients were mostly american soldiers.

4. Bella's favorite foods are French Toast and New England clam chowder.

5. I love the Spring because we always visit washington during cherry blossom time to see my aunt and uncle.

6. A french family on our block celebrates Bastille day every july.

7. Gloria Kliger's older sister moved to greenwich village in new york.

8. Among the religions practiced in india are buddhism, hinduism, and christianity.

9. Last monday the spanish consul gave a talk to the romance language club at our High School.

10. The canadians have a national holiday called dominion day which they celebrate every year on the first day of july.

11. St. Paul's church is the oldest church in our town.

12. The movie *Casablanca* was set in the Northwest section of africa.

13. Clark Kent lived in the city of metropolis, but Bruce Wade lived in Gotham city.

14. The latin name for the greek Goddess Aphrodite is venus.

EXERCISE C   Correct the capitalization in the following sentences. (Add 5 points for each correct answer.)

1. My uncle has written a book called *Everyday weather for you.*

2. Becky has a summer job working for the *norwich bugle.*

3. I saw the story about commander kay in the *wisconsin alumni Bulletin.*

4. We subscribe to the sunday edition of the *New york times,* but it never arrives until Wednesday because it comes by mail.

5. Jacqueline says her favorite animal story is *ring of bright water,* but I like *the call of the wild* much better.

6. One of the high holy days in judaism is rosh hashanah.

EXERCISE D   Supply capitals where needed. (Add 4 points for each correct answer.)

1   Herring fishing in norway lasts from january through march. The
2   best norwegian codfish come from the lofoten islands. The Norweg-
3   ians ship dried cod to mediterranean countries such as italy, and also
4   to South america. Whale fishing began around norway in the atlantic
5   ocean, but now the best whale fishing is near antarctia. In central
6   sweden, the people still wear their native costumes to church on
7   sunday. The lapps live in the far north of scandinavia. Their clothes
8   date back to the middle ages in style and look a little like santa claus
9   suits. Some lapps live in finland, a country which gained its inde-
10 pendence after world war I.

Cumulative Review

A Write the part of speech above each italicized word, using these abbreviations: *n.* for noun; *pron.* for pronoun; *adj.* for adjective; *v.* for verb; *adv.* for adverb; and *prep.* for preposition. (Add 5 points for each correct answer.)

THE THUNDER GOD

1   Thor, the greatest of the *Norse* gods, *was* the god of thunder and

2   the *bringer* of rain. He was the son of Odin and Erda, the *earth* goddess,

3   and even as a child he *displayed* monumental *rages.* He *had* a wonder-

4   ful hammer, symbolizing the *thunderbolt,* which when thrown returned

5   to him *like* a *boomerang. He* wore an *iron* glove so that he *could* hold

6   the *hammer safely* even when it was red-hot. His *chariot* was pulled

7   by two he-goats and made the sound of thunder as it *careened wildly*

8   *across* the sky. His name gives *us* Thursday.

B Put parentheses around each of the prepositional phrases in the sentences that follow. Then underline the word the phrase modifies, and write *adj.* or *adv.* in the space to the left of each sentence to show whether the phrase is used as an adjective or as an adverb. (Add 10 points for each correctly marked sentence.)

. . . . . .   1. Indira opened the door with her sore right arm.

. . . . . .   2. Corinne opened the door with the little window.

. . . . . .   3. The price for such inferior merchandise is far too high.

. . . . . .   4. The sound of a hundred singing birds awakened him.

. . . . . .   5. The horse reared and bolted across the wheat field.

. . . . . .   6. None of this petty squabbling is worth the time it takes.

. . . . . .   7. The moth flew toward the nearest light.

. . . . . .   8. They took her in a specially hired ambulance.

. . . . . .   9. They saw the movie on television.

. . . . . .   10. The tightrope artist walked with grace and agility.

C Underline the subject of each sentence once and the verb twice. Circle each complement and above it write *s.c.* for a subject complement and *d.o.* for a direct object. Some sentences are compound or have compound parts. Watch out for prepositional phrases. (Add 10 points for each correctly marked sentence.)

1. The idea of immortality has captured the imagination of many people.

2. Explorers have searched without success for the fountain of youth.

3. Sailing north from Puerto Rico, Ponce de León discovered and explored Florida for the Spanish government.

4. Natives had reported to him about a fountain of youth in Florida and Ponce de León unsuccessfully sought it.

5. Another explorer seeking immortality is portrayed by Edgar Allan Poe in "Eldorado."

6. In this poem, the knight spends his youth in fruitless search of eternal youth.

7. Immortality is not always a blessing.

8. Zeus gave immortality to Tithonus, the mortal husband of Aurora, the goddess of dawn.

9. Unfortunately, the gift did not include eternal youth.

10. Death finally appeared the real blessing to Tithonus.

D In the following paragraph, attach any sentence fragment to the sentence with which it belongs and supply the period and the capital letter to correct any run-on sentence. Insert missing commas. (Add 5 points for each correct answer.)

1   Soon after the Murphy family had moved into their new home in
2   Webster Minnesota they were invited to dinner. By the Swensons
3   their next-door neighbors. With grateful feelings for the Swensons
4   naturally the Murphys arrived for dinner with their three children
5   but a large yellow hungry-looking female dog followed them. Into the
6   house. The dog as it turned out was extremely friendly, she put her
7   paws upon the shoulders of each child in turn and licked the child's
8   face. The dog was hungry as well as friendly, in due course she went
9   to the dining room. And began licking the clean plates set out on the
10   table she entered the kitchen, and Mr. Murphy remarked, "That's a
11   remarkable animal you've got there, Mr. Swenson." The Swensons
12   were astounded, they had thought the beast belonged to their new
13   neighbors. The two families united. In driving the intruder from the
14   house. And set to work washing the dishes for dinner.

Building Vocabulary: Synonyms

Synonyms are words which have nearly the same meaning.

A synonym is really a kind of one-word definition. You use synonyms all the time, to explain the meaning of an unfamiliar word and to give your writing variety and interest. You do not need to say merely that a thing is *big,* a word for which there are many synonyms. You can say that it is *huge, gigantic, enormous, monstrous,* and so on.

Notice that synonyms have *nearly,* not exactly, the same meaning. There are no exact synonyms. Words which are synonyms for one another are simply more or less close in meaning. To find out whether two words are close enough, you test them much as you test a full definition—by trying the words out in a context.

Close synonyms can be substituted for each other in sentences.

EXAMPLE   Losing his wallet caused Whitney considerable ~~anguish~~. **pain**

In this example, the word *pain* can be substituted for *anguish* without changing the meaning. *Pain* and *anguish* are synonyms. In the following example, however, *anguish* cannot take the place of *pain:*

EXAMPLE   The **pain** caused by a sprained ankle can be almost unbearable.

Anguish cannot replace pain in this sentence because *anguish* means only one kind of pain—the mental kind. The sentence is about physical pain—the kind that an aspirin may relieve.

Study the definitions of the following words. Think of contexts in which each word might be used. Try to find at least one synonym, or one-word definition, for each word on the list.

aversion /ə vér zhən/, *n.* A feeling of keen awareness of something with, at the same time, a strong desire to be rid of it.

commend /kə ménd/, *v.* To mention a person or thing with approval.

congenial /kən jén yəl/, *adj.* Easy to get along with because of similar tastes or interests; of a group of persons, getting along well together.

congregate /kóng grə gāt/, *v.* To come together in a crowd.

futile /fy-ǘ təl/, *adj.* Not producing any result whatever.

inevitable /in év ə tə bəl/, *adj.* Impossible to prevent; sure to happen.

potent /pót nt/, *adj.* Of persons, having great power and authority; of ideas or other impersonal things, very strong, influential, or effective.

restrict /ri stríkt/, *v.* To keep within narrow bounds.

ruthless /rǘth lis/, *adj.* Showing no pity; without mercy.

thwart /thwaurt/, *v.* To oppose someone's purpose and keep it from being carried out.

127

EXERCISE Each word in italics is a synonym for one of the words presented in this lesson. In the space to the left, write the word from this lesson that has nearly the same meaning as the italicized word. (Add 10 points for each correct answer.)

.... 1. Dorothea Dix campaigned against the *unmerciful* treatment of patients in mental institutions.

.... 2. Universal human misery is one of the *unavoidable* results of modern warfare.

.... 3. Most cats have a *dislike* for soap and water.

.... 4. The speaker's most *powerful* argument for democracy was that it is more efficient than totalitarianism.

.... 5. I found the club members a *friendly* group and decided that I would like to join them.

.... 6. Because our dog is inclined to frighten mail carriers and small children, we have had to *limit* him to the backyard.

.... 7. It is *useless* to think that you can master any skill without hard work and plenty of practice.

.... 8. After school, we often *gather* at the drugstore across the street.

.... 9. Ann Story believed that she could help *prevent* a British takeover of Vermont.

.... 10. I am sure that Mrs. Hutchinson will *praise* me for the clarity of my essay.

REVIEW EXERCISE Some of the italicized words in the following sentences are used incorrectly. In the space to the left of each sentence write an *I* if the word is incorrectly used and a *C* if it is used correctly. (Add 20 points for each correct answer.)

.... 1. We *refuted* Wilburforce's arguments so effectively that he had to agree with us.

.... 2. The actors were so *audible* that even in the front row we could not hear them.

.... 3. People who become *hysterical* are usually so quiet that no one notices them.

.... 4. In most states, you must be sixteen to be *eligible* for a driver's license.

.... 5. Oxygen is *superfluous* for life as we know it.

Spelling: Words Containing the Suffixes –ly and –ness

Suffixes enable you to get multiple use from English words. If you know the base word *polite,* for example, you can make the words *politely* and *politeness* simply by adding the suffixes *–ly* and *–ness.* Fortunately, these two useful endings cause few spelling problems. Examine the two lists of words below.

–ly	*–ness*
mad + ly = madly	deaf + ness = deafness
brief + ly = briefly	pleasant + ness = pleasantness
cool + ly = coolly	thin + ness = thinness
final + ly = finally	plain + ness = plainness
wide + ly = widely	strange + ness = strangeness
complete + ly = completely	hoarse + ness = hoarseness
heavy + ly = heavily	kindly + ness = kindliness
stingy + ly = stingily	drowsy + ness = drowsiness

From your examination of the two lists above, can you make up two rules about adding *–ly* and *–ness?*

Here are the two easy rules:

When adding the suffixes *–ly* and *–ness* to a base word (except if the word ends in *y*) do *not* change the spelling of the base word.

If the base word ends in *y*, change the *y* to *i* before adding *–ly* or *–ness.*

EXCEPTIONS   truly   duly

In what way are these two words exceptions? (The spelling of the base words *true* and *due* is changed when *–ly* is added.)

EXERCISE A   Join each base word and its suffix to form a new word. Write the new word in the blank. Apply the two rules you have learned. (Add 10 points for each correct answer.)

1. dark + ness = ...   6. weary + ness = ...

2. natural + ly = ...   7. due + ly = ...

3. brave + ly = ...   8. trustful + ness = ...

4. messy + ness = ...   9. incomplete + ness = ...

5. beautiful + ly = ...   10. day + ly = ...

EXERCISE B   Mentally add either *–ly* or *–ness* to the base word in parentheses that comes after each sentence below. Then write the new word in the blank space in the sentence. (Add 10 points for each correct answer.)

1. Angela was sorry that she had spoken . . . . to her friend. (angry)

2. My brother's . . . . is one of his worst traits. (stubborn)

3. Their homework is . . . . quite neat. (general)

4. The dog's . . . . was frightening. (fierce)

5. Spiders treat their insect victims . . . . (cruel)

6. Your . . . . this morning was understandable. (tardy)

7. Did you close the letter with " . . . . yours"? (Sincere)

8. No, I used "Yours . . . ." instead. (true)

9. Patty broke the new vase . . . . (accidental)

10. The storm came on with great . . . . (sudden)

EXERCISE C Use any five of the new words you made for Exercise A in separate, short, original sentences. (Add 20 points for each correct answer.)

1. . . . .

2. . . . .

3. . . . .

4. . . . .

5. . . . .

REVIEW EXERCISE Mentally add –ing to each word below. Then write the –ing word, correctly spelled, in the blank. (Add 10 points for each correct answer.)

1. smile . . . . 6. dye . . . .

2. die . . . . 7. promise . . . .

3. explore . . . . 8. vie . . . .

4. complete . . . . 9. shine . . . .

5. hesitate . . . . 10. dance . . . .

CHAPTER EIGHT

A Verb Agrees with Its Subject

People who say *we does* or *the car run* make a very obvious mistake in *subject-verb agreement*. In writing and speaking, you must be careful to make the subject and verb of a sentence or clause agree in number.

LESSON 64

Singular and Plural

A noun or pronoun may refer to one thing or to more than one thing. The difference is called a difference in the *number* of the noun or pronoun. Most nouns and personal pronouns show a change in number by a change in the form of the word.

When a word refers to one person, place, thing, or idea, it is singular in number. When a word refers to more than one, it is plural in number.

Most nouns change from singular to plural by adding *s* or *es* to the singular form of the word, but some change in other ways. A few nouns do not change at all—the plural form is exactly the same as the singular form. In the following examples, the changes from singular to plural are printed in red.

SINGULAR	PLURAL	SINGULAR	PLURAL
athlete	athletes	knife	knives
house	houses	ox	oxen
box	boxes	goose	geese
address	addresses	sheep	sheep

Other words like *goose* that form the plural by a vowel change are *man* (*men*), *woman* (*women*), *mouse* (*mice*), and *foot* (*feet*).

The personal pronouns are entirely different in the singular and plural, except for *you,* which never changes.

SINGULAR	I, me	you	he, she, it; him, her, it
PLURAL	we, us	you	they, them

EXERCISE A In front of each of the words below, write *S* or *P* to show whether the word is singular or plural. (Add 5 points for each correct answer.)

_P_ 1. birds   _S_ 8. cloud   _P_ 15. laundries

_S_ 2. clock   _P_ 9. scarves   _S_ 16. ribbon

_P_ 3. loudspeakers   _P_ 10. radios   _P_ 17. lice

_S_ 4. bicycle   _P_ 11. women   _P_ 18. waltzes

_P_ 5. they   _S_ 12. sink   _S_ 19. mouse

_P_ 6. losses   _S_ 13. he   _P_ 20. leaves

_P_ 7. teeth   _P_ 14. children

EXERCISE B In the following passage, circle all of the singular nouns and pronouns. There are twenty-seven of them altogether. Underline all of the plural nouns and pronouns. There are twenty-three of them altogether. When in doubt about a word, ask whether it means just one thing or more than one. (Add 2 points for each correct answer.)

1   Before people understood the laws of the universe, they thought

2   the world was inhabited by spirits. Some of these spirits were good

3   and some were evil. Spirits were thought to inhabit natural objects.

4   Belief in some of these good and bad spirits has, to an extent,

5   carried over to the present day, forming the basis of superstitions.

6   Despite scientific discoveries, black cats, cuckoos, and snakes are still

7   considered objects of fear by many people. A common English

8   superstition is that it is unlucky to sweep dirt out the front door.

9   To do this is to sweep away good fortune. Some French people

10   believe that touching iron breaks bad luck. A common German

11   superstition is that no fire can come where a stork has a nest. An

12   Italian superstition maintains that snakes are guardians of buried

13   treasure. A common American belief is that to break a mirror means

14   seven years of bad luck. Many folks feel that a four-leaf clover and

15   a rabbit's foot bring good luck.

132

Matching the Verb to Its Subject

There is a very good reason for paying attention to the *number* of a noun or pronoun. Rather often, the form of a verb depends on the number of its subject, which may be a noun or pronoun.

A verb agrees with its subject in number.

SINGULAR   Martha walks to school every day. She likes the fresh air. The new road bypasses the town. Stronghart boxes at the Y.

PLURAL   The girls walk to school every day. They like the fresh air. The new roads bypass the town. The boys box at the Y.

In the examples, notice that when the subject is singular (*Martha, She, road, Stronghart*) the verb, too, is singular in number. (The *s* or *es* ending often occurs in verbs that are singular in number.) When the subject is plural (*girls, they, roads, boys*) the verb is plural.

The important helping verbs *to have* and *to do* agree with their subjects just as other verbs do.

SINGULAR   Frances has always liked swimming.
He certainly does eat a hearty breakfast.

PLURAL   They have always liked swimming.
His brothers certainly do eat a hearty breakfast.

That troublesome verb *to be* has more forms than any other verb and therefore more chances for errors in subject-verb agreement. Study the forms of *to be* and be sure you know them by heart.

SINGULAR	PLURAL	SINGULAR	PLURAL
(I) am	(we) are	(I) was	(we) were
(you) are	(you) are	(you) were	(you) were
(he, she, it) is	(they) are	(he, she, it) was	(they) were

The most common error that occurs with *to be* is the use of the singular forms *is* and *was* with the plural pronoun *they* or with a plural noun.

NONSTANDARD   They *was* almost sure to win.
Hurry! The geese *is* getting out.

STANDARD   They were almost sure to win.
Hurry! The geese are getting out.

EXERCISE A   Determine the number of the subject in each sentence. Then find the correct one of the two verbs given in parentheses that agrees with the subject in number. Underline the correct verb. (Add 10 points for each correct answer.)

1. Fifties rock (<u>is</u>, are) once again popular with the record-buying public.

2. People (listens, <u>listen</u>) to the music of Elvis Presley and Fats Domino.

3. My mother (<u>has</u>, have) a collection of records from her high-school days.

4. She (<u>owns</u>, own) a recording of Elvis Presley singing "Love Me Tender."

5. The record (<u>is worth</u>, are worth) much money today.

6. Many revival groups (plays, <u>play</u>) fifties rock.

7. Some groups (sounds, <u>sound</u>) very good.

8. I (prefers, <u>prefer</u>) the original fifties groups to the revival groups.

9. Two friends (has planned, <u>have planned</u>) a fifties nostalgia party.

10. The party (<u>seems</u>, seem) a great idea to me.

EXERCISE B   Change each subject from singular to plural or from plural to singular. Also change the verb so that it agrees with the subject in number. (Add 20 points for each correct sentence.)

A. Clouds cover the sky along the horizon.

A cloud covers the sky along the horizon.

1. A man was running frantically away from the fire.

Men ran frantically away from the fire.

2. The city closes the beaches in September.

The cities close the beaches in September.

3. They like to daydream about faraway places.

She likes to daydream about faraway places.

4. Last summer I was at the beach almost every day.

Last summer we were at the beach almost every a

5. The elm trees have been growing here for a century.

The elm tree has been growing here for a century.

Watch Out for Phrases!

When the verb comes right after the subject, there is usually no problem in deciding what form the verb should have. But in many sentences, the subject and the verb are separated by various modifiers, and these modifiers can be confusing. Prepositional phrases, in particular, cause problems. A phrase containing a *plural* noun may follow a *singular* subject; or a phrase containing a *singular* noun may follow a *plural* subject. In such cases, the verb agrees with the subject, as in any other sentence.

The number of a subject is not changed by a prepositional phrase following the subject.

EXAMPLES Shadows (from the castle wall) fall across the lawn.
(plural subject, plural verb)
One girl (from that whole group of schoolgirls) insists on walking.
(singular subject, singular verb)
One bad apple (in a basket of good ones) often spoils the rest.
(singular subject, singular verb)

The parentheses around the phrases in the examples should remind you of an important point: the subject of a sentence is never found in a prepositional phrase. The noun or pronoun in a phrase modifying this subject has no effect on the verb, which must still agree in number with its subject.

Most people have a natural impulse to make the verb agree with the noun that comes closest in front of it, but this impulse can cause errors when that noun happens to be part of a prepositional phrase. To avoid such errors, mentally drop out the prepositional phrase. Then find the verb and its subject and *make them agree*.

EXERCISE A Each of the following sentences contains one or more phrases modifying the subject. Cross out these adjective phrases and underline the subject once and the verb twice. (Add 10 points for each correctly marked sentence.)

A. Dozens ~~of pigeons from the pen on the roof~~ fly in circles.

1. One person ~~among the new members~~ objects to the proposal.

2. All of the cows ~~in the herd~~ turn their backs to the storm.

3. Hope ~~of rescue for the three students~~ diminishes hourly.

4. A few <u>pieces</u> ~~of this candy~~ rightfully <u>belong</u> to Laura.

5. The <u>book</u> ~~with the pictures~~ <u>contains</u> material on Africa.

6. The <u>height</u> ~~of the two brothers~~ <u>surprises</u> people.

7. The <u>committee</u> ~~of property-owners~~ <u>meets</u> here tomorrow.

8. Several <u>people</u> ~~with folding chairs and camp beds~~ <u>were</u> <u>waiting</u> patiently at the head of the ticket line.

9. <u>Tourists</u> ~~in Mexico~~ often <u>find</u> Aztec relics.

10. <u>Students</u> ~~at our junior high school~~ <u>start</u> school at eight thirty.

EXERCISE B In the following paragraph, there are two forms for most verbs. Cross out the one which does not agree with the subject. If in doubt, mentally drop out the prepositional phrases and find the subject of the verb. (Add 10 points for each correct answer.)

MARTIANS, ANYONE?

1 Scientists at a leading American university (~~has~~, have) been col-
2 lecting jokes. In their opinion, jokes about outer space (reveal, ~~re-~~
3 ~~veals~~) our hidden fears of the unknown. Perhaps a civilization on
4 one of the distant planets (has, ~~have~~) grown more powerful than ours.
5 If invaders from one of these older and wiser civilizations (come,
6 ~~comes~~) to earth, will we know how to stand up to them? Questions
7 of this kind apparently (worry, ~~worries~~) us. According to the scientists,
8 jokes about space invaders (calm, ~~calms~~) our inner fears. Often, the
9 invader in these jokes (~~turn~~, turns) out not to be so smart after all.
10 A little story about two Martians especially (~~amuse~~, amuses) me. The
11 creatures from Mars walk up to a parked car and (order, ~~orders~~) it
12 to take them to its leader. The parked car says nothing. Finally, one
13 Martian, after repeated threats, (~~kick~~, kicks) the car and breaks its
14 headlights. "Shame on you!" says the other Martian. "You should
15 never hit a person with glasses!"

Problems with Pronouns

Any word that takes the place of a noun is called a *pronoun.* Certain kinds of pronouns called *indefinite pronouns,* cause problems in subject-verb agreement. Some of these pronouns are always plural in meaning while others are always singular in meaning, but their number is not always clear when they are modified by prepositional phrases. To avoid mistakes, you must know which pronouns are plural and which are singular.

The following pronouns are singular and take a singular verb: anybody, anyone, each, either, everybody, everyone, neither, nobody, no one, one, somebody, someone.

When they are used as subjects, these singular pronouns are often followed by prepositional phrases that contain plural nouns. In such cases, there is a natural tendency to make the verb agree with the plural noun rather than with the singular pronoun. This is because the object of the preposition comes after the pronoun subject and is therefore closer to the verb.

NONSTANDARD	Each of the hamsters *have* been fed. (*Hamsters* is in a prepositional phrase and cannot be the subject of the verb.)
STANDARD	Each of the hamsters has been fed.
NONSTANDARD	Everyone on both teams *are* out to win.
STANDARD	Everyone on both teams is out to win.

Notice that most of these singular pronouns contain the idea of "one" —any*one,* any*body,* and so on. These pronouns are used to mean just one out of a group or the members of a group thought of individually, one at a time. As subjects, therefore, these singular pronouns require singular verbs (anyone *is,* anybody *was*).

To avoid mistakes in using a singular pronoun, mentally drop out any prepositional phrase that follows it. This will show at once the correct form of the verb to use.

NONSTANDARD	Each one of these color slides *belong* to my mother.
STANDARD	Each one (of these color slides) belongs to my mother.

The following pronouns are plural and take a plural verb: both, few, many, several.

EXAMPLES	Both of the boys have lost their bicycles.
	Several of us want to go on a class picnic.

EXERCISE A Put parentheses around any prepositional phrase that follows an indefinite pronoun. Then find and underline the subject of the sentence once and draw two lines under the correct one of the two verb forms given in parentheses. (Add 10 points for each correct sentence.)

A. One (of my brothers) (work, works) in Alaska.

1. Both (of these games) (bore, bores) my father.

2. Neither (of the cows) (was, were) a prize winner (at the state fair).

3. Either (of your suggestions) (for the meeting) (suit, suits) me.

4. Everyone (from nine) (to ninety) (is, are) going (to the parade).

5. Few, however, ever (stay, stays) (to the end) (of the program.)

6. Surely someone (in one) (of these classes) (do, does) know the answer.

7. No one (from outer space) (has, have) landed (in our backyard.)

8. Each (of these fortunate young people) (has, have) won a trip (to Death Valley) (with all expenses paid.)

9. Several (of the best-known English poets) (is, are) buried there.

10. Anyone (with a love) (of mystery stories) (enjoy, enjoys) Agatha Christie's books.

EXERCISE B Some of the verbs in the following sentences do not agree with their subjects. Cross out any incorrect verb and write the correct form above it. (Add 10 points for each correct answer.)

1. Neither of the two researchers were aware of the problem.

2. Everyone in the room ~~were~~ *was* talking at once.

3. Every spring the apples from this one tree fills several baskets.

4. A story in the newspapers recently ~~tells~~ *told* of a prize cabbage weighing forty-two pounds.

5. Several members of my class ~~has~~ *have* been absent this week.

6. Two bales of wastepaper ~~was~~ *were* lying in the middle of the road.

7. A pound of feathers weigh as much as a pound of gold.

8. The clothes for our family all come from the same store.

9. One of these stories was very funny.

10. A box of old coins were buried at the foot of a large oak tree.

More Practice in Subject-Verb Agreement

EXERCISE A In each of the following sentences, underline the subject and *cross out* the incorrect form of the word in parentheses. (Add 5 points for each correctly marked sentence.)

1. Each of us (has, have) been frightened by horror movies at one time or another.

2. One of the most popular monsters (is, are) the Frankenstein monster.

3. Mary Wollstonecraft Shelley, wife of one of the greatest English poets, (was, were) the author of the novel *Frankenstein*.

4. Many movies about the Frankenstein monster (has, have) been made.

5. Boris Karloff, often considered the king of the monster movies, (acts, act) in the first of this series of movies.

6. Several monsters from folklore (has, have) been portrayed in movies.

7. Each of the many viewers (has, have) a favorite.

8. A psychologist studying these movies (has, have) claimed that Dracula is the most frightening.

9. Dracula, prince of the vampires, (was, were) supposed to live in Transylvania.

10. The reflection of vampires (does, do) not appear in mirrors.

11. According to legend, the strong scent of garlic plants (is, are) used as protection against vampires.

12. The Wolf Man, another of the monsters portrayed in movies, (has, have) several problems.

13. Only wolf's bane, a legendary plant found exclusively in the Himalayan highlands, (prevents, prevent) his turning into a wolf at nightfall.

14. Larry Talbot, while in human form the gentlest of people, (does, do) not want to become a wolf.

15. Talbot, because of a curse of the gypsies, usually (frightens, frighten) himself as often as he does his audience.

16. Few in my age group (has, have) not seen at least one horror movie.

17. Many of the stations on television (airs, air) them late at night.

18. Several of my friends from the movie club at school (enjoys, enjoy) them most in darkened theaters.

19. The screams from the crowd (~~adds,~~ add) to the excitement.

20. If you ask me, a bag of popcorn, eaten while watching them, (makes, ~~make~~) horror movies much less frightening.

EXERCISE B Some of the verbs in the following paragraph are incorrect because they do not agree in number with their subjects. Cross out any incorrect verb and write the correct form above it. (Add 10 points for each correct answer.)

FOOD FOR THOUGHT

1   The members of an unusual British garden club specializes in giant
2   vegetables. Every year an exhibit of their largest and best-looking
3   vegetables is held in London. The size of many of the vegetables
4   at this show seem almost unbelievable to the outsider. One of the
5   prize-winning cabbages, for example, weigh in at forty-two pounds.
6   A cabbage of this size is large enough to feed an average family for
7   an entire week—provided, of course, that everyone in the family are
8   fond of cabbage. One member of the club holds the pumpkin record
9   with an oversized vegetable weighing over a hundred pounds. (Not
10   one of the members have yet tried to make it into a jack-o'-lantern.)
11   Several nearly as big has been exhibited in the past. Naturally,
12   produce of other types do not reach the mammoth proportions of
13   the pumpkins and cabbages, but it is still quite amazing. Carrots the
14   size of a person's arm are not uncommon. Prize-winning pods of peas
15   have frequently attained a length of nine or ten inches. Stalks of
16   asparagus resembles drumsticks—*bass* drumsticks. The people re-
17   sponsible for these huge legumes are not built on the same scale.
18   Many of them, in fact, seems rather small in comparison with the
19   things they grow. Perhaps this is because only a few actually eat their
20   giant vegetables. Unfortunately, the biggest and handsomest ones
21   among these giants, with a rare exception, does not taste as good
22   as those of normal size.

Turned-around Sentences

The most common way of putting a sentence together is with the subject first, followed by its verb. In certain kinds of sentences, however, this order is reversed—the verb, or part of it, comes first and then the subject. Sentences of this kind may lead you into errors in agreement. To avoid such errors, you must think ahead to the subject and make the verb agree with it.

HERE AND THERE

When the subject follows the verb, as in sentences beginning with here and there, be especially careful to determine the subject and make the verb agree with it.

EXAMPLES   Here is something to remember me by. (*Something* is the subject.)

There are eleven bananas in that bunch. (*Bananas* is the subject.)

You can make sure that the subject and verb agree by mentally reversing the sentence, putting the subject first.

NONSTANDARD   There *was* two men under the bridge. (plural subject, singular verb)

STANDARD   There were two men under the bridge. (= *Two men were under the bridge*—plural subject, plural verb)

The contractions *here's* and *there's* are short for *here is* and *there is.* Use them only with singular subjects.

NONSTANDARD   *There's* (= There is) those girls from Elmwood School.
STANDARD   There are those girls from Elmwood School. (plural subject, plural verb)

An adverb phrase is often placed first in a sentence for emphasis. When the phrase begins the sentence, it has the same effect as *here* and *there.*

EXAMPLES   Under the bridge stand two men.
At the bottom of the hole was a tiny, new-born rabbit.

QUESTION SENTENCES

In sentences that ask a question, the subject may come after the verb, or between two parts of a divided verb. To check subject-verb agreement, turn the sentence around in your mind, putting the subject first.

EXAMPLES   Has Maxwell lost his gloves again?   (= *Maxwell has lost?*)
Where are Paula's glasses?   (= *Glasses are where?*)

EXERCISE A   In each of the following sentences, underline the subject once and then underline twice the correct form of the verb in parentheses. (Add 10 points for each correct sentence.)

1. There (go, goes) the ships with all their flags flying.

2. At the top of the hill (stand, stands) a beautiful old church.

3. Down the runway and out over the bay (roar, roars) the two jets.

4. (There's, There are) not many cookies left in the jar.

5. (Do, Does) the children never get tired of running around?

6. At the bottom of the rubbish heap there (was, were) a box of valuable gems.

7. On the lawn (lie, lies) the shells of three broken birds' eggs.

8. There (is, are) only three clarinet players in the entire band.

9. (Has, Have) the preference of the members been expressed?

10. There (was, were) several moths hiding in the clothes closet.

EXERCISE B   Correct any error in subject-verb agreement by crossing out the incorrect verb and writing the correct form above it. (Add 10 points for each correctly marked sentence.)

A. ~~Where's~~ *Where are* the eggs for Uncle Findley's breakfast?

1. In an album on the top shelf there is some pictures of my mother.

2. Where is that book about the space program?

3. There's several boys waiting for you on the front steps, Emilio.

4. Here at last was an opportunity for Lee to express herself.

5. Have one of the girls brought in the mail yet?

6. Here's the oranges you wanted.

7. There was too many raisins in that pudding for Maxine's taste.

8. Does either of your parents play tennis?

9. On the beach beside the dock there was three or four canoes.

10. There has been various explanations for the mayor's change of heart.

DON'T and DOESN'T

Many people mix up the contractions *don't* and *doesn't,* particularly in everyday speech. Remember that *don't* is short for *do not* and that *doesn't* is short for *does not. Don't* should be used with all plural subjects and the pronouns *I* and *you. Doesn't* should be used with all singular subjects except *I* and *you.*

SINGULAR	PLURAL
(I) don't	(we) don't
(you) don't	(you) don't
(he, she, it) doesn't	(they) don't
(Gabriella) doesn't	(the girls) don't

NONSTANDARD   Willis *don't* like maple syrup.
STANDARD   Willis **does**n't like maple syrup.   (*doesn't = does not,* the correct form for a singular subject)

NONSTANDARD   The people in the lifeboat *doesn't* need our help.
STANDARD   The people in the lifeboat **do**n't need our help.

(*don't = do not,* the correct form for a plural subject)

EXERCISE A   Change each singular subject to a plural subject and each plural subject to a singular subject. Make the verb agree, as in the example. (Add 10 points for each correct sentence.)

A. The cats like fish. *The cat likes fish.*

1. Your books don't interest me. *Your book doesn't interest me.*
2. This girl doesn't tell lies. *These girls don't tell lies.*
3. The elephant doesn't forget. *The elephants don't forget.*
4. The boxes don't weigh much. *The box doesn't weigh much.*
5. He just doesn't like me. *They just don't like me.*
6. The oxen don't eat enough. *The ox doesn't eat enough.*
7. Travelers don't usually ask directions. *A traveler doesn't usually ask directions.*
8. The geese don't remember. *The goose doesn't remember.*
9. She doesn't give much help. *They don't give much help.*
10. The mouse doesn't like the cheese. *The mice don't like the cheese.*

EXERCISE B   Underline the subject of each sentence and then fill in the blank with the correct contracted form of *to do—don't* or *doesn't.* Check the answers by trying out the uncontracted forms (*do not, does not*) before filling in the blank. Watch out for prepositional phrases. (Add 4 points for each correct sentence.)

A. A can of peanuts *doesn't* last long at our house.

B. Three quarts of milk *don't* just vanish into thin air!

1. A whole bag of sugar *doesn't* last more than a few days.

2. Rita Mazour *doesn't* want to go to the circus.

3. *Doesn't* anyone like fried chicken?

4. Julie's parents *don't* let her watch television very much.

5. This book about Sojourner Truth *doesn't* belong to me.

6. *Doesn't* the Beck family live here any more?

7. Those bikes across the street *don't* belong to any of us.

8. The hairdresser *doesn't* always do such a good job.

9. The rings of Saturn *don't* look so clear in a photograph.

10. Everyone *doesn't* enjoy skating as much as Viola.

11. The conductor of the orchestra *doesn't* want to change.

12. Chris *doesn't* want to play the flute any more.

13. Any friend of yours *doesn't* need to apologize.

14. People *don't* often refuse credit for good deeds.

15. The actors in a play *don't* all have big parts.

16. *Doesn't* a person with responsibilities ever take chances?

17. It simply *doesn't* matter to me which movie we go to.

18. The moon *doesn't* look so large when it's low in the sky.

19. The people from the moving company *don't* want to wait.

20. This ball-point pen *doesn't* look much like mine.

21. The girls in my class *don't* all think as you do.

22. I *don't* understand the problem, and Loomis *doesn't* either.

23. A person with red hair *doesn't* always have a fiery temper.

24. *Doesn't* some solution to your problems seem likely?

25. Good grades *don't* just happen by themselves.

What About Compound Subjects?

A compound subject is made up of two or more subjects that have the same verb. Usually, the parts of a compound subject are connected by the conjunction *and, or,* or *nor.* The number of the subject depends on which of these conjunctions is used.

Compound subjects joined by <u>and</u> are plural and take a plural verb.

This rule contains no surprises. The *and* joins two things together, making two—which is what we mean by plural.

EXAMPLES   The westbound <u>express</u> **and** the freight <u>train</u> <u>**were**</u> derailed.

An old <u>oak</u> **and** an American <u>elm</u> <u>**stand**</u> beside the front door.

When we use *and* to join the parts of a compound subject, we mean both together. When we use *or* (or *nor*), on the other hand, we mean one or the other but *not both.*

Singular subjects joined by <u>or</u> or <u>nor</u> are singular and take a singular verb.

EXAMPLES   The <u>lilac</u> **or** the <u>honeysuckle</u> <u>**has** been moved</u>.

The <u>road</u> to the right **or** the <u>one</u> straight ahead <u>**leads**</u> to home.

Sentences of this kind often begin with *either* (or *neither*).

EXAMPLES   **Either** the <u>tug</u> **or** the <u>ferry</u> <u>**was**</u> off course.

Neither the <u>geranium</u> **nor** the <u>fern</u> <u>**gets**</u> enough water.

If both parts of a compound subject joined by *or* or *nor* are plural, the verb must, of course, be plural also.

EXAMPLE   <u>Soldiers</u> **or** <u>police</u> officers <u>**were** blocking</u> all the exits.

EXERCISE A   Underline the correct one of the two verb forms in parentheses. (Add 10 points for each correct answer.)

TWO ANGLERS

1   Betty Salvio and Pat Huggins, the girl who lives next door to

2   her, (like, <u>likes</u>) to go fishing at Lake Pewauskee. Either Betty or

3   Pat generally (get, <u>gets</u>) someone to take them out to the lake, and

4   then they and all the other people who are fishing there (<u>spend</u>,
5   spends) hours at a time just catching a couple of catfish. Once in a
6   while some old-timer or some really devoted angler (claim, <u>claims</u>)
7   that there are bass in that lake, but neither Betty nor Pat (<u>has</u>,
8   have) ever caught one, nor (<u>has</u>, have) anyone else ever caught any.
9   Neither their lack of success nor the thought of how much time they
10 have wasted there, however, (keep, <u>keeps</u>) them from going back to
11 try again. Some people from the city and even a few local business
12 executives (<u>think</u>, thinks) nothing of spending their whole vacation
13 there. Either the hook or the bait they use (is, <u>are</u>) no good, appar-
14 ently. At any rate, Betty and Pat freely (<u>admit</u>, admits) their failure
15 at Lake Pewauskee.

EXERCISE B   Some of the verb forms in the following sentences are incorrect. Cross out each incorrect verb and write the correct form above it. Remember that *or* and *nor* mean *either one but not both*. Singular subjects joined by *or* or *nor* require the singular form of the verb. (Add 10 points for each correctly marked sentence.)

1. The toy soldier and the stuffed dog was thrown away in the trash.
2. Either the car or the boat are going to be sold.
3. The throw rug and the slipcover were both made by hand.
4. The house next door and one around the corner is painted pink.
5. Either the dog or the cat have to stay outside.
6. The sounds of helicopters and horns from trucks in the street wakes me up too early some mornings.
7. Either a cold or some kind of virus infection have kept him in bed since Monday.
8. Neither the battery nor the generator are out of order.
9. The leaves and the grass trimmings has to be raked today.
10. Students and teachers were running off in all directions.

Chapter Review

EXERCISE A   In each of the following sentences, put parentheses around the prepositional phrases, underline the subject, and circle the correct one of the two verb forms given in parentheses. (Add 4 points for each correct sentence.)

1. One (of the Christmas tree ornaments) (is, are) hand painted.

2. His passion (for Bartlett pears) (grow, grows) (with each bite).

3. (Was, Were) neither (of the two orchestral pieces) very well played?

4. Everyone (from the New England states) (is, are) to leave (at once).

5. Three (of the rarest coins) (in the collection) (was, were) missing.

6. Several (of the students) (from the classes) (in the new wing) (do, does) a very good job (with a paintbrush).

7. The light (from the neon signs) (in the store windows) (is, are) bright enough.

8. Everyone (in our choral group) obviously (love, loves) (to sing).

9. The prices (of the various items) (on sale) (at the department store luggage counter) (was, were) clearly marked.

10. Anyone (with a desire) (to play) and patience enough (for practicing) during long stretches (of time) (make, makes) a good piano student.

11. (In the center) (of each table) (sit, sits) a bowl (of fresh flowers).

12. Where (was, were) the other members (of the committee) (during the meeting?)

13. (After the meeting) only two bars (of chocolate) (was, were) left.

14. (Has, Have) Lisa or Margrit told you (about the news broadcast) yet?

15. No one (from our school) ever (go, goes) there.

16. Alfie and Louise sometimes (do, does) their homework together.

17. (Don't, Doesn't) several (of you) leave (for camp) tomorrow?

18. Two sticks and some pebbles (was, were) the child's only toys.

19. Neither Ethel nor that friend (of hers) (want, wants) (to leave) yet.

20. (Behind the band) (come, comes) a few (of the most elaborate floats).

21. Each (of the five contestants) (wants, want) the prize.

147

22. <u>Neither</u> (of the pets) (was, (were)) housebroken.

23. <u>Both</u> (of the girls) (from that club) (has, (have)) won trophies.

24. The <u>beneficiaries</u> (from the insurance policy) (has, (have)) not received as much money as expected.

25. The <u>solution</u> (to the mysteries) surrounding the crimes (was, (were)) given (by the detective)

EXERCISE B The following paragraph contains various errors of verb agreement. Cross out each incorrect verb and write the correct form above it. (Add 10 points for each correct answer.)

FLOWERY TALK

1   There's something about large flowers that Joyce ~~don't~~ *doesn't* like.

2   Their showiness and their size ~~repels~~ *repel* her. Cannas is her pet peeve.

3   Cannas, in her frequently expressed opinion, isn't good for anything

4   but public parks. Marigolds and zinnias, on the other hand, make

5   a fine floral display. Either of these kinds of flowers are good for

6   large or small gardens. There ~~are~~ *is* nothing finer than a bed of red

7   zinnias. But she really comes into her glory at the sight of a fine bed

8   of asters. This kind of flower ~~are~~ *is* her favorite. It ~~don't~~ *doesn't* matter to her

9   what color they are. At the far end of her lawn are a bed of the finest

10   asters in town. Everyone with an interest in gardening recognizes

11   them as prize winners. Not many of them ~~is~~ *are* for picking, however.

Cumulative Review

A In the following sentences, find the simple subject, verb, and direct object or subject complement. (Not every sentence contains a direct object or a subject complement.) Above the appropriate word, write *s.* for subject; *v.* for verb; *d.o.* for direct object; *s.c.* for subject complement. (Add 10 points for each correctly marked sentence.)

1. John Smith became the leader of the colony at Jamestown, Virginia.

2. Pocahantas helped the settlers in Jamestown.

3. Most farms in the colonies were very small in the early days.

4. The only roads were narrow trails among the trees.

5. River transport became particularly important.

6. Many towns used boats for contact with other places.

7. Almost everything was made by hand.

8. Even nails were produced by blacksmiths.

9. Most settlers grew their own food.

10. In time, trade with the interior grew more important.

B Put parentheses around the prepositional phrases in the following sentences and underline the word each phrase modifies. Then write *adj.* above the phrase if it is used as an adjective and *adv.* if it is used as an adverb. (Add 20 points for each correct sentence.)

1. The colonies along the south Atlantic coast gained their income from tobacco and rice plantations.

2. With their new and sometimes persecuted religious beliefs, the Quakers needed the religious freedom of the New World.

3. Colonies were not established in Georgia until the eighteenth century.

4. In 1733, General Oglethorpe arrived in Georgia with a group of settlers and named the area after the British king.

5. The Pilgrims landed at Plymouth in 1620 and sought the friendship of the Wampanog tribe.

C The following paragraph contains sentence fragments and run-on sentences. Correct the errors by adding or crossing out periods and capital letters as necessary. (Add 10 points for each correct answer.)

149

1   Robin Hood is a legendary figure of English folklore his story can

2   be traced back to the fourteenth century. When writers first mention

3   his name. He has been identified with various real people. Among

4   them a twelfth-century earl. The Earl of Huntingdon. It is more likely

5   that he was simply a fictional character. There are many English folk

6   songs about Robin Hood, he was supposed to be a great archer who

7   lived with his men in Sherwood Forest. Near Nottingham, England.

8   They robbed the rich and gave money to the poor. As everyone

9   knows. Thanks to modern versions of the legends, members of the

10   band are familiar figures, today most young people have read about

11   Friar Tuck, Little John, and Robin Hood's other "merry men." The

12   story will remain forever fresh. While there are new readers. To en-

13   joy it.

D The following paragraph is full of comma and capitalization errors. Correct them all. (Add 4 points for each correct answer.)

A CAREER IN BRIEF

1   William E. b. Du Bois was born in Great barrington Massachusetts,

2   on February 23 1868, three years after the War Between the states.

3   After High School, he won a scholarship to Fisk university. As Editor

4   of the school paper the *Fisk herald* he called on his fellow students

5   to organize a crusade to wipe out race prejudice. In 1888, harvard

6   university awarded him a scholarship and Du Bois proudly accepted.

7   At harvard, he studied Philosophy and History. Du Bois was one

8   of the founders of the National association for the advancement of

9   colored people. He wrote over twenty books. Among them was *The*

10   *souls of black folk.*

Building Vocabulary: Antonyms

Simply knowing a new word is no use unless you can make it part of your *active* vocabulary—so that you can recall it readily and use it correctly to say what you mean. It helps to think of words in pairs or groups. We remember and use words with similar meanings *as a group*. You can also think of words with *opposite* meanings as a group.

Antonyms are words that have nearly opposite meanings.

EXAMPLE   The newspaper charged that the chief of police was not
honest.
The newspaper charged that the chief of police was **corrupt**.

In this example, *corrupt* and *honest* are antonyms—they have nearly opposite meanings. Notice that *corrupt* makes a more forceful statement than merely saying *not honest.*

Besides being useful for expanding your vocabulary, antonyms can also help you to explain word meanings briefly and clearly. Many words do not have close synonyms. For example, it is rather roundabout to say that *passive* means "enduring without offering resistance," but if you say that *passive* means "not active" or is "the opposite of *active,*" the meaning is at once clear.

Study the following word meanings and try to think of a suitable antonym for each word.

brevity /brév ə tē/, *n.* The use of few words to express something.

confirm /kən fə́rm/, *v.* To say or prove that a doubtful statement is true.

dismal /díz məl/, *adj.* Dark and gloomy; miserable.

disperse /dis pə́rs/, *v.* To scatter or to go away to different places.

dubious /dū́ bē əs/, *adj.* Doubtful; not sure of the outcome of something.

fickle /fík əl/, *adj.* Not sticking to things; likely to change.

lenient /lḗ nē ənt/, *adj.* Not harsh or severe; easygoing in matters of discipline.

predecessor /préd ə sés ər/, *n.* One who has gone before someone in a job or an office.

tactful /tákt fəl/, *adj.* Careful about doing and saying the right thing to others.

transient /trán shənt/, *adj.* Lasting for only a short time.

EXERCISE   Underline the antonym for each italicized word—the word that has nearly the opposite meaning. (Add 10 points for each correct answer.)

1. *Brevity* is not usually one of a politician's notable qualities.
   antonym: (a) friendliness (b) intelligence   (c) <u>wordiness</u>

2. The government would not *confirm* the news of our landing on Mars.
   antonym: (a) approve   (b) <u>deny</u>   (c) release

151

3. A pessimist can usually see the *dismal* side of any situation.
   antonym: (a) <u>cheerful</u>   (b) easy   (c) inexpensive

4. The mayor stood on the steps of City Hall and asked the crowd to *disperse* and return to their homes.
   antonym: (a) continue   (b) <u>gather</u>   (c) agree

5. Carmen was extremely *dubious* about the outcome of the game.
   antonym: (a) <u>certain</u>   (b) happy   (c) fearful

6. During the fall, the weather tends to be *fickle*.
   antonym: (a) weak   (b) hard-working   (c) <u>constant</u>

7. Mr. Agnew is inclined to be too *lenient* with his class.
   antonym: (a) <u>strict</u>   (b) unkind   (c) serious

8. Our principal's *predecessor* was the author of several textbooks.
   antonym: (a) enemy   (b) successor   (c) <u>co-worker</u>

9. A *tactful* person would not have mentioned my poor grade on the test.
   antonym: (a) <u>unkind</u>   (b) stupid   (c) blunt

10. Fortunately, the lion's interest in Martha Magnuson was *transient*.
    antonym: (a) eager   (b) <u>permanent</u>   (c) hostile.

REVIEW EXERCISE   In the space to the left of each word group write the letter of the best meaning for the italicized word. (Add 10 points for each correct answer.)

h.	1. Two events may *coincide*.	a. sure to happen
c.	2. a *fantastic* idea	b. to destroy completely
j.	3. an *intricate* plan	c. strange, odd, fanciful
b.	4. The Huns *annihilated* the army.	d. the act of giving in
f.	5. leading to *homicide*	e. a complete disaster
g.	6. an *aversion* to cats	f. killing of a human being
i.	7. engaged in an *altercation*	g. strong dislike
d.	8. a *concession* to weakness	h. to happen together
e.	9. an overwhelming *catastrophe*	i. angry argument
a.	10. an *inevitable* result	j. extremely complicated

Spelling: Does It End with -cle or -cal?

When writing words such as *miracle* or *comical,* do you find yourself hesitating when you get to the *–c* near the end of the word and wondering whether to use *–cle* or *–cal?* These endings *sound* alike, so your ear is of no help in deciding. There is a way, however, that will help you to choose the correct ending for such words.

Examine the two lists of words below. All the words in list *1* end in *–cle;* all those in list *2* end in *–cal.*

	1			*2*	
article	bicycle		musical	physical
icicle	tentacle		medical	political
popsicle	obstacle		logical	practical

Besides their endings, what else do the words in list *1* have in common? What do those in list *2* have in common? All of the words in *1* are nouns; all those in *2* are most commonly used as adjectives. To prove this, try using each word in a sentence.

Therefore, if the word you want to spell is a noun, you can be fairly certain that *–cle* is the correct ending. If the word is used primarily as an adjective, then you are right if you spell its ending *–cal.* In fact, *–cal* (actually *–ical*) was the ending used in Latin to turn a noun into an adjective. This helps explain why our English words that end in *–cal* are generally adjectives, and why there is usually a noun form for every adjective that ends in *–cal.* The adjective *musical* has the noun form *music;* the adjective *political* has the noun form *politics;* the adjective *logical* has the noun form *logic.*

EXERCISE A   For each of the following nouns, there is a related adjective ending in *–cal* (or *–ical*). In the blanks provided, write the related adjectives. If you need to, use your dictionary. (Add 10 points for each correct answer.)

EXAMPLE   grammar *grammatical*

1. alphabet ... *alphabetical*
2. critic .... *critical* ....
3. rhythm .... *rhythmical*
4. mathematics ... *mathematical*
5. magic ... *magical* ....
6. method ... *methodical*
7. tropics ... *tropical* .
8. Bible ... *Biblical* ....
9. myth ... *mythical* ..
10. poet ... *poetical* .....

EXERCISE B   Complete each unfinished word part in the sentences below by writing *–cle* or *–cal,* whichever is right, in the blank. Decide whether the incomplete word is used mainly as a noun or as an adjective; then apply the information you have learned. (Add 10 points for each correct answer.)

1. A tricycle is a vehi *cle* with three wheels.

2. An appendectomy is a surgi *cal* operation.

3. A trillion dollars is an astronomi *cal* sum of money.

4. A wastepaper basket is a recepta *cal* for trash.

5. My sister has a very mechani *cal* mind.

6. The sunset was a gorgeous specta *cle* to see.

7. Celia and Jennifer are identi *cal* twins.

8. The lists are arranged in numeri *cal* order.

9. On the lens of the microscope was a tiny parti *cle* of dust.

10. First draw a horizontal line and then a verti *cal* one.

EXERCISE C   Use any five of the adjectives you made for Exercise A in separate, original sentences. (Add 20 points for each correct answer.)

1. *You are to put the words in alphabetical order.*
2. *The patient was in critical condition.*
3. *The magical rabbit disappeared.*
4. *In the tank were tropical fish.*
5. *In the religion book it said to read the Biblical account.*

REVIEW EXERCISE   Study the words below, and be prepared to write them from dictation. Remember the two easy rules about adding the suffixes –ly and –ness to a base word. (Add 4 points for each correct answer.)

1. thinness *thin*
2. daily *day*
3. stubbornness *stubborn*
4. coolly *cool*
5. tardiness *tardy*
6. beautifully *beautiful*
7. drowsiness *drowsy*
8. truly *true*
9. strangeness *strange*
10. angrily *angry*
11. suddenness *sudden*
12. stingily *stingy*
13. kindliness *kindly*
14. naturally *natural*
15. weariness *weary*
16. cruelly *cruel*
17. finally *final*
18. plainness *plain*
19. sincerely *sincere*
20. completely *complete*
21. duly *due*
22. hoarseness *hoarse*
23. heavily *heavy*
24. messiness *messy*
25. generally *general*

CHAPTER NINE

Using Verbs Correctly

Verbs express action, and action takes place in time—in the past, in the present, in the future. When you want to connect a particular action with a particular time, you can do so by adding a helping verb or by changing the form of the verb itself or by both together. Knowing which form of a verb to use and when to use it is often vital to clear and effective communication. The rules for using the various verb forms correctly are the subject of this chapter.

LESSON 76

How Verbs Show Time

The verbs in English can express past, present, and future time and a great many variations of these as well. The grammar term for the time which a verb shows is *tense*. All the tenses which a verb needs to express can be made by means of four basic verb forms.

The four basic forms of a verb are the present, the present participle, the past, and the past participle. These basic forms are called the principal parts.

PRESENT	PRESENT PARTICIPLE	PAST	PAST PARTICIPLE
walk	(is) walking	walked	(have) walked
hope	(is) hoping	hoped	(have) hoped
study	(is) studying	studied	(have) studied

As you can see, the present participle of a verb always ends in *–ing* and is always used with some form of *to be* as a helping verb. The present participle (plus its helping verb) is used to express continuing action.

The past participle (plus some form of *to have* as a helping verb) is used to express past action.

The helping verb *to be* is also used with the past participle of some verbs to show that the subject *receives* the action of the verb.

EXAMPLES   The lesson **was** learned.   The wood **has been** burned.

The verb *to do* is used as a helping verb with the present principal part in questions and for emphasis.

EXAMPLES   **Did** you study the assignment?   Honestly, I **did** study it!

The past principal part expresses past time all by itself, without the aid of a helping verb. It is sometimes called the *simple past,* to distinguish

155

it from the past tense formed from the helping verb *to have* plus the past participle. Notice the difference in meaning between the two past tenses.

SIMPLE PAST   Yesterday I **studied** my assignment. (completed past action)

PAST WITH HELPER I **have studied** the assignment, but I still don't understand it. (past action still affecting the present)

EXERCISE The verbs in the following sentences are printed in italics. In the space to the left of each sentence, write *present* if the sentence is about action taking place in the present time or *past* if the sentence is about action taking place in past time. (Add 5 points for each correct answer.)

Past   1. Our parents *complained* about the mess in our room.

Present   2. We *like* to study on the floor.

Past   3. We *had scattered* our books all over the place.

Present   4. Mom and Dad *have decided* to get us a new bookcase.

Present   5. We *need* a place for our books.

Present   6. We *are running* out of space.

Present   7. A neighbor of ours *owns* a furniture store.

Past   8. Our parents *had asked* him to build a bookcase for us.

Past   9. The bookcase *was delivered* within two days.

Present 10. The new bookcase *contains* all our books.

Present 11. Our room *has been looking* much neater these days.

Present 12. In fact, it *has* never *seemed* so tidy before.

In the remaining sentences, change the italicized verb to the present tense if it is in the past tense or to the past if it is in the present. Write the verb in the space to the left of the sentence.

bakes   13. Julia Child *baked* a superb dessert.

poured 14. I sometimes *pour* too much cream on my cereal.

enjoyed 15. We *enjoy* our new book by Virginia Hamilton.

use   16. A few *used* rancid butter to keep the mosquitoes off.

worked 17. For a little while, I *work* on my homework assignment.

visit   18. Julia *visited* Mexico in the winter.

danced 19. Natalia Makarova *dances* beautifully.

played 20. Annette *plays* a good chess game.

SEE and COME, DO and GO

The verbs that you studied in the preceding lesson are called *regular verbs*. All regular verbs form their past and past participle in exactly the same way—by adding *-d* or *-ed* to the present form of the verb.

The verbs that you are now going to study do not form their past and past participle according to this simple rule. Because they do not follow the rule, these verbs are called *irregular verbs*. Some of the most common and most useful verbs in English are irregular verbs. Notice how the principal parts of these four differ from those of the regular verbs. (Since the present participle of *all* verbs is formed by adding *-ing* to the present form, the present participle is omitted from this table of irregular verbs.)

PRESENT	PAST	PAST PARTICIPLE
see	saw	(have) seen
come	came	(have) come
do	did	(have) done
go	went	(have) gone

People sometimes mistakenly use the simple past when they should use the past participle (I have *went* home). A more common mistake is the use of the past participle for the simple past. A past participle can act as the verb of a sentence only if it has a helping verb.

| NONSTANDARD | We *seen* Jacqueline at the movies. |
| STANDARD | We saw Jacqueline at the movies. |

The example can also be corrected by the insertion of a helping verb, although the sentence would then have a slightly different meaning.

ALSO STANDARD   We have seen Jacqueline at the movies. (The sentence now suggests that seeing Jacqueline is still important in some way, even though it happened in the past.)

The big thing to remember is that a past participle by itself cannot be the verb of a sentence.

| NONSTANDARD | I *come* back from camp yesterday. |
| STANDARD | I came back from camp yesterday. |

| NONSTANDARD | Julius *done* all his homework last night. |
| STANDARD | Julius did all his homework last night. |

| NONSTANDARD | Mark *seen* the parade. |
| STANDARD | Mark saw the parade. |

EXERCISE A In the following items, fill in the blanks with the past participle of the italicized verb when there is a helping verb, or with the simple past if there is no helping verb. (Add 5 points for each correct answer.)

1. *See:* I have ...*seen*........
2. *Do:* They ...*did*...........
3. *Come:* He has ..*come*....
4. *Go:* You ......*go*...........
5. *See:* She ...*saw*..........
6. *Go:* We have ..*gone*......
7. *Come:* They ...*came*.....
8. *Come:* You ...*came*......
9. *See:* He was ..*seen*......
10. *Do:* It was ...*done*.......

11. *Come:* I have ..*come*....
12. *Do:* I ...*did*.............
13. *See:* We ...*saw*...........
14. *Do:* It has been ..*done*....
15. *See:* You have ...*seen*....
16. *Come:* We did ...*come*...
17. *Come:* I ....*came*........
18. *Do:* She has ...*done*......
19. *See:* We were ...*seen*....
20. *See:* It has been ..*seen*....

EXERCISE B Write the correct past form of the verb in parentheses in the blank that follows it. Use the past participle after any form of the helping verb *to be* or *to have*. (Add 10 points for each correct answer.)

A TRIP TO THE AQUARIUM

1 Marcia's science class (go) *went* on a trip to the aquarium. Most
2 of the class had (go) *gone* to the aquarium last year, but they
3 hadn't (see) *seen* all of the creatures there. The science teacher
4 and two parents (come) *came* along on the trip. They (see) *saw*
5 a baby whale, called a calf, that weighed about fourteen thousand
6 pounds. One of the parents who had (come) *come* on the trip
7 explained that the calf might double its size within a year. Marcia
8 said that she had (do) *done* a report on whales last year. According
9 to her research, some whales have been (see) *seen* to reach
10 maturity within three years. The class left the aquarium and (go)
11 *went* back to school at about two o'clock. Most of the class felt
12 that of all the things they had (do) *done* that year in school, they
13 had enjoyed the trip to the aquarium the most.

Sorting Out the Problem Verbs

Many of the irregular verbs fall into groups because they form the simple past and the past participle in a similar way. The verbs in this lesson, with two exceptions, form the simple past by changing the vowel (*e, i, o,* or *u*) to *a*. They form the past participle by changing the vowel to *u*.

PRESENT	PAST	PAST PARTICIPLE	PRESENT	PAST	PAST PARTICIPLE
begin	began	(have) begun	drink	drank	(have) drunk
run	ran	(have) run	ring	rang	(have) rung
sing	sang	(have) sung	swim	swam	(have) swum

A common error in using these verbs is to confuse the past participle with the simple past. To be sure of avoiding this error, memorize the three principal parts of the irregular verbs listed above. As you repeat these principal parts to yourself, always say the helping verb *have* with the past participle as a reminder that it can never be used as a verb unless it has a helping verb with it.

NONSTANDARD	STANDARD
It *begun* to rain.	It **began** to rain.
He *run* all the way home.	He **ran** all the way home.
She *sung* beautifully.	She **sang** beautifully.

Less often, people make the opposite error, using the simple past in place of the past participle.

NONSTANDARD	STANDARD
We have *drank* our milk.	We have **drunk** our milk.
Someone has *rang* the bell.	Someone has **rung** the bell.
They have *swam*.	They have **swum**.

The verb *to bring*, the seventh verb in this lesson, is one of the two exceptions mentioned above.

PRESENT	PAST	PAST PARTICIPLE
bring	brought	(have) brought

Because *bring* rhymes with *sing* and *ring*, we sometimes make the mistake of thinking that its principal parts follow the same pattern. So far as standard English is concerned, however, there are no such words as *brang* or *brung*.

| NONSTANDARD | Carol *brang* the book back. | She has *brung* it too soon. |
| STANDARD | Carol **brought** the book back. | She has **brought** it too soon. |

Another common and important irregular verb, *to think,* works in the same way as *to bring,* even though it rhymes with *drink.* There are no such words as *thunk* or *thinked.*

| PRESENT | PAST | PAST PARTICIPLE |
| think | thought | (have) thought |

EXERCISE A In the following items, fill in the blanks with the past participle of the given verb when there is a helping verb, or with the simple past if there is no helping verb. (Add 10 points for each correct answer.)

1. They (swim) *swam.*
2. It was (drink) *drunk*
3. We (run) *ran*
4. She has (ring) *rung*
5. They (sing) *sang.*

6. They were (begin) *begun*
7. It (ring) *rang*
8. He (drink) *drank*
9. It was (sing) *sung*
10. I have (swim) *swum*

EXERCISE B In the following sentences, write the correct past form of the verb given in parentheses before each blank. Remember to use the past participle after a helping verb. (Add 10 points for each correct answer.)

1. The movie has just (begin) *begun*
2. She (drink) *drank* so much salt water that she was sick.
3. The prisoner was (bring) *brought* before the judge in handcuffs.
4. He had (swim) *swum* halfway to shore before they rescued him.
5. Dorothy has (sing) *sung* the lead in *Madame Butterfly.*
6. Both the front and the back doorbells were (ring) *rung*
7. Gordon (think) *thought* for a long time before making up his mind.
8. The wild ponies (run) *ran* into the canyon.
9. Every single bottle of soda was (drink) *drunk* at the party.
10. The name (ring) *rang* a bell somewhere in his memory.

Nine Problem Verbs

All the irregular verbs in this lesson have past participles that end in *–en,* and all of them form their simple past by changing their vowel (or vowels) to a long *o.* These verbs fall into two groups, depending on whether the past participle is formed from the present or from the simple past.

PRESENT	PAST	PAST PARTICIPLE	PRESENT	PAST	PAST PARTICIPLE
break	broke	(have) broken	choose	chose	(have) chosen
speak	spoke	(have) spoken	freeze	froze	(have) frozen
steal	stole	(have) stolen			

The most common error in the use of these verbs consists of putting the simple past in place of the past participle.

NONSTANDARD	STANDARD
The clock was *broke.*	The clock was broken.
They have *chose* Ben.	They have chosen Ben.
My nose was *froze.*	My nose was frozen.

The second group forms the past participle by adding *–n* to the present. In three of these past participles, the vowel changes from long to short to make it easier to pronounce.

PRESENT	PAST	PAST PARTICIPLE	PRESENT	PAST	PAST PARTICIPLE
drive	drove	(have) driven	ride	rode	(have) ridden
write	wrote	(have) written	take	took	(have) taken

NONSTANDARD	We have *drove* twelve miles.	Janet has *rode* on a camel.
STANDARD	We have driven twelve miles.	Janet has ridden on a camel.

EXERCISE A In the following sentences, write the correct past form of the verb given in parentheses before each blank. Remember to use the past participle after a helping verb. Check all answers against the tables of verbs given above. (Add 5 points for each correct answer.)

1. The candy bar was (break) *broken* in two.

2. He had (choose) *chosen* three books to read during vacation.

3. The sheep was butchered and (freeze) *frozen* for them.

4. After the leader has (speak) *spoken*, we will all leave.

5. Pearl Bailey had (steal) *stolen* the show.

6. The birds were (drive) *driven* away by the cats.

7. Ynes Mexia (ride) *rode* a balsa raft on one of her botanical expeditions.

8. Sylvia's essay has (take) *taken* the lead in the contest.

9. The winning paper was (write) *written* by someone I know.

10. Armand dropped his watch and (break) *broken* it.

11. They have (choose) *chosen* three people to make the trip to Canada.

12. The ice cubes (freeze) *frozen* in fifteen minutes.

13. The lecturer had (speak) *spoken* on the same subject before.

14. Peter Pan had (steal) *stolen* the secret of eternal youth.

15. They (drive) *drove* the cattle along the Chisholm Trail.

16. Pia has even (ride) *ridden* in an elephant's howdah.

17. Demetrius has (take) *taken* first prize for beards.

18. Louisa May Alcott (write) *wrote* many stories before *Little Women* was published in 1868.

19. By November the pond will have (freeze) *frozen*

20. Maxine had been (drive) *driven* half crazy by that woodpecker.

EXERCISE B In the following paragraph, underline the correct form of each verb in parentheses. (Add 10 points for each correct answer.)

1   When the box was finally (broke, <u>broken</u>) into, it was obvious that

2   someone had already (stole, <u>stolen</u>) everything of value. A list of the

3   contents was (wrote, <u>written</u>) inside the cover and made it clear that

4   the thieves had (took, <u>taken</u>) only the important things. Each of us

5   (<u>chose</u>, choosed) something from the things that were left, but Paul

6   (<u>spoke</u>, speaked) for all of us when he said that it was a great disap-

7   pointment. The box itself was (took, <u>taken</u>) back to base camp, and

8   we must now leave soon or the river will be (froze, <u>frozen</u>). We have

9   by now (rode, <u>ridden</u>) hundreds of miles through this wilderness, and

10   the trip has (took, <u>taken</u>) the whole year, all for nothing.

More Problem Verbs

Verbs like *to tear* (past participle: *torn*) and *to blow* (past participle: *blown*) seem at first glance to have little resemblance to the other irregular verbs you have studied so far. In fact, however, they are not really so different. The verbs in this lesson form their simple past by a vowel change and their past participle by adding *–n* or *–en* either to the present or to the simple past.

PRESENT	PAST	PAST PARTICIPLE	PRESENT	PAST	PAST PARTICIPLE
blow	blew	(have) blown	fall	fell	(have) fallen
know	knew	(have) known	give	gave	(have) given
throw	threw	(have) thrown			

The typical error in using *give* is the use of the present form for both the simple past and the past participle.

NONSTANDARD	STANDARD
Yesterday, Dad *give* me a lecture.	Yesterday, Dad gave me a lecture.
I have *give* too much time.	I have given too much time.

There is a tendency to treat *blow, know,* and *throw* as if they were regular verbs (adding *–ed* to form the past and the past participle). In standard speech and writing, however, you should use only the forms shown in the table.

NONSTANDARD	We *knowed* all along.	Jerry has *throwed* it away.
STANDARD	We knew all along.	Jerry has thrown it away.

Our second group of verbs consists of just two. Both form the past participle by adding *–n* to the simple past, omitting the final *e*.

PRESENT	PAST	PAST PARTICIPLE	PRESENT	PAST	PAST PARTICIPLE
tear	tore	(have) torn	wear	wore	(have) worn

NONSTANDARD	STANDARD
The letter was *tore* in little pieces.	The letter was torn in little pieces.
I have *wore* my new shoes.	I have worn my new shoes.

EXERCISE A Write in the blank the correct past form of the verb in parentheses. Remember to use the past participle after a helping verb. (Add 10 points for each correct answer.)

1. The hurricane has (blow) *blown* down dozens of trees.

2. I have (know) _known_ the professor for many years.

3. He was (throw) _thrown_ for a loss by the surprise question.

4. They have (give) _given_ me real encouragement.

5. The pencil was (wear) _worn_ down to a stub.

6. They have already (throw) _thrown_ out all the old papers.

7. Her sudden appearance (give) _gave_ me a great shock.

8. I certainly (know) _knew_ that he wasn't feeling well.

9. They all (blow) _blew_ on their hands to keep them warm.

10. Carlos suddenly (throw) _threw_ him a curve ball.

EXERCISE B Some of the italicized verbs in the following sentences are in the correct form and some are not. Draw a line through each incorrect verb and write the correct form above it. (Add 4 points for each correct answer.)

1. For years Mom refused, but at last she ~~give~~ _gave_ in.

2. The wind ~~blowed~~ _blew_ down a large tree and *tore* a hole in the fence.

3. If I'd ~~knowed~~ _knew_ you were coming, I'd have ~~give~~ _given_ a party.

4. Melanie has ~~fell~~ _fallen_ from her horse and has ~~tore~~ _torn_ her pants.

5. The outfielder had ~~threw~~ _thrown_ the ball to the pitcher, who then *threw* it home.

6. Caitlin has ~~blowed~~ _blown_ out all the candles on her birthday cake.

7. His little joke has ~~throwed~~ _thrown_ the meeting into an uproar.

8. The thorns have ~~tore~~ _torn_ a hole in Alice's stocking.

9. I *knew* I should have ~~wore~~ _worn_ blue jeans.

10. They had ~~gave~~ _given_ the address to Baayork, but she ~~throwed~~ _threw_ it away.

11. Mrs. Dougherty has always ~~gave~~ _given_ heavy homework assignments.

12. The wind, apparently, had ~~blew~~ _blown_ the car out of control.

13. If Archie had ~~knew~~ _known_ what to expect, he'd not have *torn* out into the street like a scared rabbit.

14. They ~~give~~ _gave_ me the final notice about a month ago.

15. The woman had ~~tore~~ _torn_ the letter in little pieces and had ~~threw~~ _thrown_ it away.

16. If Jerry had ~~knowed~~ _known_ how high he was, he might have ~~fell~~ _fallen_.

Using SIT and SET Correctly

Do you *sit* in a chair or *set* in a chair? Do you *sit* a package down on the counter or *set* it down? The problem here is not one of mixing up the correct forms of a verb but of confusing two different irregular verbs which sound alike and have somewhat related meanings. In order to use *sit* and *set* correctly, you must be clear about how they differ in meaning.

The verb sit means to sit down, to occupy a seat, or to rest.

These are the principal parts of *to sit.*

PRESENT	PRESENT PARTICIPLE	PAST	PAST PARTICIPLE
sit	(is) sitting	sat	(have) sat

The verb set means to place or to put something down.

These are the principal parts of *to set.*

PRESENT	PRESENT PARTICIPLE	PAST	PAST PARTICIPLE
set	(is) setting	set	(have) set

As a rule, *to set* must have a direct object to complete its meaning. *To sit,* on the other hand, usually does *not* take a direct object.

SET   Conrad set the pan on the stove.   Set me down, please.

SIT   Barnaby **sat** and **sat**   The pan is **sitting** on the stove.

EXERCISE A   In the space to the left of each sentence, write the letter *a* or *b* to show the meaning of the italicized verb or participle:

>   *a*—means *to sit down, to occupy a seat, to rest*
>   *b*—means *to place* or *to put something down*

If in doubt about which verb is which, look at the lists of principal parts for *sit* and *set* above. (Add 10 points for each correct answer.)

a.   A. The paint bucket was *sitting* on the highest shelf.

b.   B. We will *set* up the Ping-Pong table in the basement.

a   1. The elderly woman *sits* in her chair all day and reads.

b   2. Annie Peck, the first to climb Mount Coropuna in Peru, *set* a "Votes for Women" pennant on its summit.

b   3. In the fall, we *set* out three dozen tulip bulbs.

a. 4. "Someone," said the bear, "has been *sitting* in my chair!"

b. 5. The costume will be *set* out on your bed, ready to be put on.

b. 6. Floyd *set* his glasses on the end of his nose and went to work.

a. 7. Imagine our surprise when we found a small spaceship *sitting* in the backyard.

a. 8. I couldn't have *sat* there another minute.

a. 9. We *sat* in the waiting room for two hours.

b. 10. Sam *sets* his books down anywhere in the house.

EXERCISE B   Underline the correct one of the two verbs in parentheses in each sentence. Determine what meaning the verb must have in the sentence. (Add 5 points for each correct sentence.)

1. The old dog (<u>sits</u>, sets) in the sun and dreams.

2. Hearing a floorboard creek, Meredith (<u>sat</u>, set) up in bed.

3. (Sitting, <u>Setting</u>) down the tools, the plumber relaxed for a moment.

4. I suppose the books will just (sit, <u>set</u>) there until I put them away.

5. Dad (sat, <u>set</u>) Andrea on her feet and told her to walk.

6. This machine (sits, <u>sets</u>) the pins up automatically.

7. Norman and Beatrice had (<u>sat</u>, set) down on the porch swing.

8. They were still (<u>sitting,</u> setting) there an hour later.

9. The first one to (sit, <u>set</u>) a dime on edge will win.

10. The girls all (<u>sit,</u> set) in the front of the class.

In the remaining sentences, cross out *set* if it is used for *sit* or *sit* if it is used for *set* and write the correct form of the proper verb above the error. Write *C* above any form of sit or set used correctly.

11. You can't expect to s͡et [C] the world to rights while ~~setting in~~ *sitting* an easy chair.

12. After dinner, Uncle Marc ~~sets~~ *sits* in his favorite chair and reads the paper.

13. Just ~~sit~~ *set* the cup on the table, ~~set~~ *sit* down, and stop worrying.

14. Mildred sat [C] in a stiff chair with a bored expression on her face.

15. She ~~sat~~ *set* the hat on her head again, but it still did not set [C] properly.

16. After ~~sitting~~ *setting* the coffee back on the stove, Nancy ~~set~~ *sat* down to talk.

Using LIE and LAY Correctly

Like *sit* and *set, lie* and *lay* sound alike and have somewhat similar meanings. To keep this troublesome pair straight, you must pay attention to the difference in meaning and know the principal parts.

The verb lie means to recline or to remain lying down.

These are the principal parts of *to lie.*

PRESENT	PRESENT PARTICIPLE	PAST	PAST PARTICIPLE
lie	(is) lying	lay	(have) lain

The verb lay means to put down or to place something.

These are the principal parts of *to lay.*

PRESENT	PRESENT PARTICIPLE	PAST	PAST PARTICIPLE
lay	(is) laying	laid	(have) laid

Like the verb *to set, to lay* usually needs a direct object to complete its meaning. The verb *to lie,* on the other hand, usually does *not* have a direct object.

OBJECT   Lay the package on the counter.   She laid her book aside.

NO OBJECT   The package lies on the counter.   The book lay in a chair.

EXERCISE A   In the space to the left of each sentence, write the letter *a* or *b* to show the meaning of the italicized verb or participle:

> *a*—means *to recline* or *to remain lying down*
> *b*—means *to put down* or *to place something*

If in doubt, notice whether the verb has a direct object and is therefore a form of *to lay,* meaning *to put down.* If the verb does not have a direct object, it will usually be a form of *to lie,* meaning *to recline.* (Add 10 points for each correct answer.)

a   A. On Saturdays, I often *lie* in bed until ten o'clock.

b   B. The contractor is already *laying* the foundation for our school.

a   1. Isabella *lay* on the sand and watched the waves.

b   2. Alex *laid* his sunglasses on the sand and went for a swim.

b   3. The movers were *laying* the carpet in the wrong room.

b   4. Terri left her bike *lying* in the snow until it rusted.

a. 5. The donkey has *lain* down and will not get up.

b. 6. The children had *laid* their stockings by the fireplace.

a. 7. The farmhouse *lies* at the foot of the next hill.

b. 8. In the evening, Miles *lays* out his clothes for the next day.

a. 9. The laundry will have *lain* there for a week when we finally get around to collecting it.

b. 10. The orderly saluted and *laid* the message on the general's desk.

EXERCISE B Underline the correct one of the two verbs in parentheses. To make sure, decide what meaning the verb must have in the sentence and check the lists of principal parts on the preceding page. (Add 5 points for each correct answer.)

1. If George (lies, lays) there any longer, he will catch cold.

2. Mother and I had already (lain, laid) our plans for the party.

3. (Lying, Laying) her book aside, Ms. Nesbitt looked expectantly at the class.

4. (Lying, Laying) down on a job is one thing no one respects.

5. The clothes had (lain, laid) too long in the sun and were faded.

6. After the cyclone, broken furniture (lay, laid) all over the room.

7. We shall (lie, lay) our flowers on the monument.

8. At the bottom of the hole, (lay, laid) a tin box of old papers.

9. A heap of rusty metal was (lying, laying) beside the barn.

10. Ambrose would get sunstroke if he (lay, laid) there any longer.

   In the remaining sentences, fill each blank with the correct past form of *to lie* or *to lay*.

11. The inn . . *lay* . . . near where the village store once stood.

12. I. M. Pei, the architect, . . . *laid* . . out the plans for the building.

13. The lion . . *laid* . . . . down its prey and . *laid* . . . . down beside it.

14. The bugle still . *lay* . . . . where Lee had . *laid* . . . . it.

15. You should have . . *laid* . . . . that silly project aside long ago!

16. Shirley . . *laid* . . . out her clothes for the next day before she . . . . *lay* . down in bed.

17. The smog . *lay* . . . . over the city.

© 1977 HBJ

168

Chapter Review

EXERCISE A Write the simple past and the past participle of each of the verbs below. Some of them are regular verbs. (Add 4 points for each correct item.)

	PAST	PAST PARTICIPLE		PAST	PAST PARTICIPLE
1. see	saw	seen	14. write	wrote	written
2. give	gave	given	15. throw	threw	thrown
3. lie	lay	lain	16. take	took	taken
4. come	came	come	17. blow	blew	blown
5. fall	fell	fallen	18. bring	brought	brung × brought
6. go	went	gone	19. wear	wore	worn
7. freeze	froze	frozen	20. set	set	set
8. drink	drank	drunk	21. swim	swam	swum
9. run	ran	run	22. lay	laid	laid
10. speak	spoke	spoken	23. begin	began	begun
11. steal	stole	stolen	24. do	did	done
12. drive	drove	driven	25. choose	chose	chosen
13. ride	rode	ridden			

EXERCISE B In the following sentences, cross out the incorrect one of the two verb forms given in parentheses. (Add 4 points for each correct answer.)

1. The boys have (~~drank~~, drunk) two gallons of apple cider.

2. She (saw, ~~seen~~) you coming out of the auditorium.

3. The children have (~~ran~~, run) around the block twice.

4. Charlie's aunt has (~~drove~~, driven) here from Chicago.

5. Some vandals have (~~tore~~, torn) several pages out of that book.

6. The coat (~~lay~~, laid) where he had (~~throwed~~, thrown) it.

7. They apparently (did, ~~done~~) the same thing last week.

8. The three trucks (came, ~~come~~) in at the same time yesterday.

9. The wind has (blew, ~~blown~~) the shutter open.

10. We have (~~rode,~~ ridden) overnight on the bus.

11. Maybelle has (~~went,~~ gone) to buy some coffee.

12. The courageous girl has (~~swam,~~ swum) all the way across Lake Erie.

13. I have for once (~~wrote,~~ written) all the details in my report.

14. When have you usually (~~sang,~~ sung) the national anthem?

15. They have certainly (~~took,~~ taken) their time about it.

16. The picture was (~~stole,~~ stolen) some time before eleven P.M.

17. The boy was (lying, ~~laying~~) under the tree, sound asleep.

18. Why don't you (sit, ~~set~~) down and stay a while?

19. Have you (~~brung,~~ ~~brought~~) the paper in yet?

20. The boys were already half (~~froze,~~ frozen), and then it (began, ~~begun~~) to snow.

21. Near the fire, Brenda (sat, ~~set~~) the shoes she had (~~wore,~~ worn).

22. The vase has (~~fell,~~ fallen) off the table.

EXERCISE C Cross out each incorrect verb form in the following paragraph, and write the correct form above it. (Add 10 points for each correct answer.)

A CRAFT SHOW

1   We had ~~went~~ _gone_ to the craft show hoping to learn some new skills.

2   We ~~brung~~ _brought_ our own materials for the crafts in which we were inter-

3   ested. Chris wanted to learn how glass was ~~blew~~ _blown_. Laurie had ~~began~~ _begun_

4   hooking a rug and wanted to pick up some tips on how colors should

5   be ~~chose~~ _chosen_ for the best effect. Angela ~~come~~ _came_ to the show to learn about

6   stained glass construction. She had already made two small pieces

7   that she ~~lay~~ _laid_ proudly on the table. We ~~seen~~ _saw_ a silkscreen artist at work.

8   After the membership committee had ~~spoke~~ _spoken_, we accompanied the

9   artists to their work areas. They ~~done~~ _did_ their best to help us. Some

10 gave us samples of their work.

170

Cumulative Review

A   In the following paragraph, indicate the part of speech of each italicized word, using these abbreviations: *n.* for noun; *pron.* for pronoun; *adj.* for adjective; *v.* for verb; *adv.* for adverb; and *prep.* for preposition. (Add 4 points for each correct answer.)

1   Our Student Council *proposed* that *student* volunteers *help* with *this*

2   year's United Fund Drive. *They posted* a notice on all the *school*

3   bulletin boards. *Several* students came and *asked* how they could help.

4   *At* the *headquarters* of the Fund Drive, *helpers* were *needed for* the

5   *card* files, and *some* of the students came in *for* an *hour* and worked

6   *hard.* A *half-dozen* students were used as messengers on *weekends.* All

7   these volunteers *were* a big help. *Afterward,* the director *officially*

8   *thanked* the students for their aid.

B   Underline every direct object in the following sentences and circle every subject complement. (Add 10 points for each correct answer.)

1. Dad is (sleeping) better, but he still does not look (well)

2. After (the) summer, we (sent) a crate of oranges to Grandma in Montreal.

3. Grant will (eat)(a) hamburger, French fried potatoes, and a salad.

4. Every car (performed) well in the race except ours.

5. (The) cat (tasted) its food cautiously but would not eat it.

6. (The) action may (seem) foolish or unnecessary, but it is still brave.

C   In the following paragraph, there are many errors of capitalization, omitted commas, unnecessary commas, sentence fragments, and run-on sentences. Correct all these mistakes. (Add 2 points for each correct answer.)

A MONARCH'S FALL

1   Conditions in france in 1789, Made the country ripe for revolution.

2   The harvest of 1788 had been bad, the Winter of 1788–89 was

3   unusually cold. Over one hundred thousand people in paris were

4   in dire poverty, With no prospect of relief. The King Louis XVI was

5   forced to summon the french Parliament. He tried to interfere but

6   on june 23, 1789, it refused to obey him. The king decided to dismiss

7   the parliament. On that famous day July 14, 1789 the paris Mob

8   surged into the streets, And attacked the Bastille a famous Prison.

9   Its fall was the signal for peasant uprisings all over the Country. On

10 October 5, 1789 a mob marched to versailles, invaded the castle, and

11 forced the king to move to paris; for two years the Moderates ruled.

12 They drew up a modern Constitution for france, but the king and

13 Queen conspired with foreign Monarchs, and austria, and prussia,

14 invaded france. On august 10, 1792 a crowd attacked the Royal

15 palace, deposed the king and declared France a Republic. King louis,

16 a prisoner of the republic was tried and condemned to death the

17 following January. He was guillotined in public soon after, the queen

18 died later that year.

D In the following sentences, cross out the incorrect one of the two forms
given for each verb. (Add 10 points for each correct answer.)

1. Everybody in both countries (was, were) pleased by the treaty.

2. The hinges for the right-hand door (was, were) taken off.

3. Both their car and their radio (was, were) made in Germany.

4. The house and the garage at the end of the street (was, were) burned.

5. We (wasn't, weren't) in the mood for a party.

6. There (was, were) knots in it when you first got it.

7. At the back of the house (stand, stands) a toolshed and a garage.

8. Inside the box (lie, lies) a mother cat and her four kittens.

9. Either the station wagon or the truck (has, have) to turn.

10. Somebody from one of the classes (has, have) to find it.

Building Vocabulary: Choosing the Precise Word

An unabridged dictionary lists something like six hundred thousand English words, and even that large number probably does not account for all the words we have in English. With so many words to choose from, you do not have to write or speak in hit-or-miss fashion. There is usually a word that says not more or less, but exactly, what you want to say.

In choosing among words with similar meanings, choose the one that says precisely what you want to say.

EXAMPLES   When his friend finally offered help on the project, Randolph **spurned** his offer.

After he won the contest without Jake's assistance, Randolph **shunned** every place where there was a chance of meeting him.

From the context, you can tell that *spurned* and *shunned,* the words printed in red, must be fairly close in meaning—*to reject* or *to treat unkindly.* The difference in meaning is important, however. *Spurn* means "to refuse something that has been offered and to do so with contempt." *Shun* means "to avoid completely." Which word you choose depends on precisely what you want to say.

Spurn and *shun* both carry a good deal of meaning. Very often, a single, precise word can replace a whole flabby, hit-or-miss phrase. Compare these two sentences, both of which have much the same meaning.

FLABBY   The candidate *aroused strong feelings of opposition* in his listeners.

PRECISE   The candidate **antagonized** his listeners. (*Antagonized* replaces all the italicized words in the preceding example.)

Study the following definitions. In the exercise that follows, be ready to use the words in their precise meanings.

contemplate /kón təm plāt/, *v.* To consider carefully and thoughtfully: *The artist stood back from her painting to contemplate the effect.*

counteract /koún tər ákt/, *v.* To act so as to keep something from happening: *The doctor's prompt treatment counteracted the poison.*

potential /pə tén chəl/, *adj.* Possible but not yet developed; having the power to do or to become something: *Carson's careless driving is a potential menace to the community.*

shun /shun/, *v.* To avoid completely.

spontaneous /spon tắ nē əs/, *adj.* Happening naturally, without forethought or outside cause: *Laura's decision to rescue the drowning child was entirely spontaneous.*

spurn / spərn/, *v.* To refuse with contempt.

technique /tek nḗk/, *n.* The method or procedure needed to do something well: *Marion has improved her piano technique through much practice.*

tumult /tū́ mult/, *n.* Noisy confusion, as of the voices of many people milling around: *When the Eagles tied the score, the tumult in the grandstand was deafening.*

turmoil /tər moil/, n. A bothersome confusion of movement or thought, not necessarily noisy (compare with *tumult*, which always involves noise): *In the turmoil after the game, I lost my hat.*

vigilance /víj ə ləns/, n. Keen and careful watchfulness, as for danger: *Only the guard's vigilance prevented the burglars from escaping with the company's money.*

EXERCISE   In the space to the right of each sentence, write the one word from this lesson that could replace the group of words in italics. (Add 10 points for each correct answer.)

1. Scientists have devised a new *method of production* for making artificial diamonds.   1. *technique*

2. The detective *studied* the photograph *carefully and thoughtfully* for a clue to the crime.   2. *contemplate*

3. Gabriel's surprised reaction to the suggestion was, I'm sure, *without forethought.*   3. *spontaneous*

4. Last-minute cramming cannot *keep* a semester of laziness *from taking effect.*   4. *counteract*

5. As the study hall quieted, the teacher's *careful watchfulness* gradually relaxed.   5. *vigilance*

6. Sara's *possible but not yet fulfilled* talent as an artist seems very great.   6. *potential*

Complete the blanks in these sentences with words presented in this lesson. Study the context carefully and be sure to use the word with the precise meaning for the context.

7. The crowd set up a great tu *mult* .... at midnight, and in the tu *rmoil* .... the boy became separated from his parents.

8. After what he had done, the soldiers decided to s. *hun* ...... the traitor and to s. *purn* .... his attempts at friendliness.

REVIEW EXERCISE   To the left of each italicized word, write the letter of the best meaning from the list at the right. (Add 20 points for each correct answer.)

b. 1. a *colossal* statue   a. to give up formally

a. 2. *renounce* a privilege   b. huge, gigantic

d. 3. a *potent* force for good   c. gloomy, miserable

c. 4. a *dismal* personality   d. powerful, mighty

e. 5. *disperse* one's efforts   e. to scatter

Spelling: Homonyms

Have you ever written *brake* when you meant *break?* Or *sent* instead of *scent?* Mistakes of this kind are fairly common because both pairs of words *sound* alike. Therefore, your ear cannot help you to choose between them. They may *sound* alike, but they differ in both spelling and meaning.

Such words are called *homonyms.* The best way to master the correct use of homonyms is to learn their spelling and meaning at the same time. You must simply memorize them by studying them in meaningful sentences.

Here are some of the more troublesome sets of homonyms—each with a sentence illustrating correct meaning and spelling. Try to memorize them.

altar—alter
    The priest faced the *altar.*   I will *alter* the hem.
brake—break
    Release the *brake.*   You *break* the eggs.
capital—capitol
    Lima is the *capital* of Peru.   We saw the *capitol* dome.
course—coarse
    Vi has an art *course.*   His beard is *coarse.*
here—hear
    She is buried *here.*   Can you all *hear* me?
meet—meat
    I'll *meet* you later.   Rover eats only *meat.*
principle—principal
    My main *principle* is charity.   Mr. Ray is our *principal.*
sent—scent
    Sue *sent* us a gift.   I like the *scent* of roses.
stationary—stationery
    The desks are *stationary.*   Her *stationery* is blue.
through—threw
    I see *through* him.   Who *threw* that ink?

EXERCISE A   Indicate the correct definition of each word in list *1*, by writing the *letter* of the proper definition from list *2*. (Add 10 points for each correct answer.)

	1		2	
..*d.*	1. coarse	a.	the edible flesh of animals	
.*m*.	2. stationary	b.	a guiding rule	
..*f.*	3. alter	c.	a mechanism for stopping a machine	
..*a.*	4. meat	d.	rough	
..*n.*	5. hear	e.	transmitted	
		f.	official seat of government	

_k._ 6. principal
_j_ 7. break
_o_ 8. scent
_f_ 9. capital
_p_ 10. through

g. in this place
h. writing paper
i. a series of lessons in a subject
j. to smash or shatter
k. the head of a school
l. to change
m. not moveable
n. to receive sounds
o. an odor
p. having finished successfully

EXERCISE B Underline the correct word from the pair in parentheses. (Add 10 points for each correct answer.)

1. Name the (<u>capital,</u> capitol) of India.

2. When you are (threw, <u>through</u>) with the paints, may I use them?

3. Find out when we are supposed to (meat, <u>meet</u>).

4. Always apply the (break, <u>brake</u>) gently.

5. Our high school offers a (coarse, <u>course</u>) in Russian.

6. The (<u>scent,</u> sent) of apple blossoms came drifting in the window.

7. The Aztec priest stood before the stone (alter, <u>altar</u>).

8. Come (<u>here,</u> hear) immediately!

9. Plain white (stationary, <u>stationery</u>) is always in good taste.

10. Who is the assistant (<u>principal,</u> principle) of Pierson Junior High School?

EXERCISE C On a separate piece of paper, use each of the words _not_ underlined in Exercise B in a brief sentence which clearly shows its meaning. (Add 10 points for each correct sentence.)

REVIEW EXERCISE Complete each unfinished word part below by writing _–cle_ or _–cal,_ whichever is correct, in the blank. (Add 10 points for each correct answer.)

1. alphabeti _cal_
2. identi _cle_
3. obsta _cle_
4. mechani _cal_
5. politi _cal_

6. practi _cal_
7. vehi _cle_
8. magi _cal_
9. specta _cal_
10. ici _cle_

CHAPTER TEN

Getting Your Pronouns Straight

A pronoun is a word that takes the place of a noun. Personal pronouns are often used, but they are sometimes misused as well. Except for *you,* every personal pronoun has both a singular and a plural form. Except for *you* and *it,* every personal pronoun also has a subject and an object form.

SUBJECT PRONOUNS		OBJECT PRONOUNS	
I	we	me	us
you	you	you	you
he	they	him	them
she		her	
it		it	

The correct form of a pronoun is determined by its use in a sentence. The subject form is used for subjects and for subject complements; the object form is used for objects. In this chapter you will study the various situations in which pronoun problems arise.

Pronouns as Subjects

To find the subject of a sentence, you first find the verb and then ask *who?* or *what?* The answer to this question will be the subject.

EXAMPLE Did they leave you behind again? (*Who* did leave? *They* is the subject.)

Only the subject forms of the personal pronouns may be used as the subjects of verbs: I—we; you; he, she, it—they.

Most mistakes in the use of subject pronouns occur when the pronoun is part of a *compound subject*—two or more connected subjects that have the same verb. You naturally select the right pronoun form when the pronoun is used singly (she runs, we talk—*not* her runs, us talk.) When the pronoun is connected with another noun or pronoun, however, you are not always sure which form to use. The solution is to try the pronoun out by itself.

NONSTANDARD	*Him* and *me* went to the movies last night.
STANDARD	He and I went to the movies last night. (*He* went, *I* went; therefore, *He* and *I* went)

The pronoun *they* is the only one with which people often have trouble when it is not part of a compound subject. *Them* is the object form of the pronoun and cannot be used as the subject of a verb.

NONSTANDARD	*Them* are the trees I told you about.
STANDARD	They are the trees I told you about.

Notice that in a compound subject the pronoun *I* comes at the end—it is considered impolite to mention oneself first.

AWKWARD	*I,* Mary, and Ruth will bring some records.
BETTER	Mary, Ruth, and I will bring some records.

EXERCISE A   Write a suitable personal pronoun in each blank, according to the meaning of the sentence. Use a variety of pronouns, but do *not* use *it* and *you,* which never change. If in doubt, try the pronoun by itself with the verb. (Add 10 points for each correct answer.)

1. Why can't Grace and . . . . see eye to eye about Mr. Rowley?

2. In my opinion, ... and Clayton were both mistaken.

3. . . . . and . . . . are tied for first place.

4. Last week, Pia and . . . . played a joke on my sister.

5. . . . . and their silly questions make me tired.

6. . . . . and . . . . always forget their books.

7. Danny and . . . . lost our way, but our teacher and . . . . found us.

EXERCISE B   Underline the correct one of the two pronouns in parentheses. (Add 10 points for each correct answer.)

1. (She, Her) and Roberta Linsky left for Florida last night.

2. Norman, Claude, and (I, me) camped out overnight.

3. Are you or (she, her) planning to go to college?

4. Maggie, Miss Klein, and (they, them) are traveling together.

5. Why, in heaven's name, should Deborah, (she, her), or (I, me) go on another of those silly picnics?

6. (He, Him) and (I, me) are going to have a heart-to-heart talk.

7. (She, Her) and (they, them) were wearing identical hats.

Pronouns as Subject Complements

A *subject complement* is a word that follows a linking verb and serves to describe or explain the subject of the verb. When it follows some form of the linking verb *to be,* a personal pronoun may be used as a subject complement. The name, *subject* complement, should help you to remember the correct pronoun forms to use.

Use the subject forms of the personal pronouns when they follow any form of the verb to be: I—we; you; he, she, it—they.

EXAMPLES The man in the back of the bus was he.

It must have been they at the front door.

A pronoun subject complement points to the same person or thing as the subject. For this reason, sentences like those in the examples can usually be turned around and still make perfectly good sense. To make sure which pronoun is right after a form of the verb *to be,* turn the sentence around and try the pronoun out as the subject of the verb.

NONSTANDARD This year's prize winner will probably be *him.* (= *him* will be)

STANDARD This year's prize winner will probably be he. (= *he* will be)

You need to be especially watchful when the subject complement is compound. You can usually solve the problem by trying each pronoun by itself as the subject complement.

NONSTANDARD Was it Lynn, *her,* or *me* who was supposed to report?

STANDARD Was it Lynn, she, or I who was supposed to report?

(Was it *she,* Was it *I;* therefore, Was it *Lynn, she* or *I*)

The expression *it's me* is usually permissible in informal speech and writing, even though it does not follow the rule. In formal situations—and in the exercises in this book—it is better, and never incorrect, to use the subject form *I* as the subject complement.

INFORMAL The person waiting at the door was me.
FORMAL The person waiting at the door was I.

EXERCISE In the following sentences, underline the correct form of the personal pronoun in parentheses. (Add 5 points for each correct answer.)

1. The club president next year will be (she, her).

2. The last guests to arrive were Julius and (her, she).

3. The plot's chief victims were (them, they) and (we, us).

4. Must the show-offs in this class always be (he, him) and Nick?

5. The finalist might be either you or (her, she).

6. The two fastest runners have usually been (she, her) and (me, I).

7. The founders of the Journalism Club were (them, they) and (us, we).

8. It will be (he, him), (her, she), or (I, me) who will be chosen.

9. It might possibly have been (him, he) whom you met.

10. Was it Anders or (she, her) who was ahead?

11. In this class the practical jokers are usually (they, them).

12. Whatever anyone says, it is (us, we) who will take the blame.

13. It might have been you or (I, me) in that flaming wreck, Nan.

14. Was it (she, her) or Rebecca that you talked to on the train?

15. Must it always be (us, we) who do all the work?

REVIEW EXERCISE The following paragraph contains all the personal pronoun constructions you have studied up to this point. Correct any pronoun error by drawing a line through it and writing the proper pronoun form above it. (Add 10 points for each correct answer.)

DISASTROUS FUN

1 Barney Haskell and me have been good friends for years, and
2 anyone would think he'd have better sense. It was him, not I, you
3 see, who suggested that we take Charlotte and Melissa to the River-
4 side Amusement Park. Him and me had saved our money over the
5 summer and gotten our parents' permission. So, when that fateful
6 Saturday arrived, us and the girls set out with high hopes. Right away,
7 the trouble started. Melissa and Charlotte and I wanted to try all
8 the different rides, but we discovered that Barney—now he tells
9 us!—is afraid of high places. That ruled out the Jackrabbit, the Moon
10 Rocket, and the other rides that the girls and me had come for. Him
11 and Charlotte stood shoulder to shoulder, and it was him, of course,
12 who suggested a rowboat ride instead. Just as us and them were
13 getting in, it began to rain. And that was that!

Pronouns as Direct Objects

A direct object is a sentence complement, or completer, that receives the action of the verb or shows the result of the action. It answers the question *whom?* or *what?* after an action verb.

Only the object forms of the personal pronouns may be used as the objects of verbs: me—us; you; him, her, it—them.

EXAMPLES Harold lost them at the supermarket.

They took me to the party in their car.

Do not confuse a direct object with a subject complement, which requires the subject form of a personal pronoun. Remember that since a direct object receives the action of the verb, it must come after a verb that shows action—an *action* verb. A subject complement, on the other hand, comes after a form of the linking verb *to be,* which does not show action.

DIRECT OBJECT Wendell introduced us to the Dexter boys. (action verb)

SUBJECT COMPLEMENT It might have been they who told us. (linking verb)

If the direct object is compound (made up of two or more objects joined by *and, or,* or *nor*), it is not always clear that the object form of the pronoun is needed. In such sentences, you can clear up any doubt by trying each part of the compound object alone with the verb.

NONSTANDARD The coach needled Otis and *he* unmercifully.

STANDARD The coach needled Otis and him unmercifully. (needled *Otis,* needled *him;* therefore, needled *Otis* and *him*)

NONSTANDARD They invited neither May nor *I* nor any of our friends.

STANDARD They invited neither May nor me nor any of our friends. (invited *May,* invited *me;* therefore, invited neither *May* nor *me*)

EXERCISE A Fill each blank with a suitable personal pronoun, using each pronoun at least once. Do *not* use the pronouns *you* and *it.* All the pronouns needed are used as direct objects. (Add 10 points for each correct answer.)

A. His constant running back and forth wears Bill and ...*me*... down.

1. Mary's parents spoil her little sister and ....

2. The old man rowed Jerry and .... across the lake.

3. We didn't see their friends or .... at the game.

4. The pass play fooled the coach and ....

5. Before the performance, Ms. Julkins painted .... and us all red.

6. I signaled Carry and .... from the next hill.

7. The salesclerk told Lucille and .... that the book was no longer in stock.

8. Phyllis photographed Gardner and .... standing in front of the school.

9. During the night, mosquitoes kept Marty and .... from sleep.

10. Mr. Salisbury will take .... or the Mansons to the game.

EXERCISE B All of the following sentences need a complement of some kind, but some of the complements are direct objects and others are subject complements. In the space to the left of each sentence, write *LV* if the verb of the sentence is a *linking verb* (requiring a subject complement), or *AV* if it is an action verb (requiring a direct object). Underline the correct one of the two pronoun forms in parentheses. (Add 5 points for each correctly marked sentence.)

...*AV*... A. The storm hit both the Lucases and (we, <u>us</u>).

...*LV*... B. It could have been (<u>they</u>, them) or the Henleys, of course.

.... 1. Mrs. Lowell praised Louis and (I, me) to the skies.

.... 2. No, the storm did not worry (she, her) or (I, me).

.... 3. It was (she, her) and Andrea who left early.

.... 4. It never leaves (he, him) alone for a minute.

.... 5. The UFO frightened both (he, him) and (I, me).

.... 6. The only girls who saw it were (she, her) and Eve DeAngelis.

.... 7. Vinnie Orlando invited Sheila and (I, me) to the rehearsal.

.... 8. It will upset either (they, them) or Ruth, I think.

.... 9. It might have been (he, him) at the door.

.... 10. Neither Shirley nor Seymour had seen (her, she) before.

182

Pronouns After Prepositions

The noun or pronoun that comes after a preposition is called the *object* of the preposition. If we think of the matter in this way, we should have no difficulty in knowing what form of a personal pronoun to use after a preposition.

Only the object forms of the personal pronouns may be used as the objects of prepositions: me—us; you; him, her, it—them.

EXAMPLES   Martha borrowed the music from us   (*Us* is the object of the preposition *from.*)

A teacher like him would inspire anyone. (*Him* is the object of the preposition *like.*)

Do not be misled if the object of the preposition is compound. To be sure which pronoun form to use, try the pronoun separately with the preposition.

NONSTANDARD   The Jacksons came after Maxwell and *I.*

STANDARD   The Jacksons came after Maxwell and me   (After *Maxwell,* after *me;* therefore, after *Maxwell* and *me.*)

EXERCISE A In each of the following sentences, underline the prepositional phrase and circle the correct one of the two pronouns in parentheses. (Add 5 points for each correct answer.)

A. I have been talking to Emilio and (he, him).

1. My aunt brought gifts for my brother and (I, me).

2. We were sitting behind Olivia and (he, him).

3. Did you go with Ellen or (her, she)?

4. Has anyone heard from the Morgans and (they, them)?

5. The bus left without our teacher and (us, we).

6. I have confidence in the coach and (them, they).

7. We agreed to stay near the guide and (she, her).

8. The others arrived before Terry and (me, I).

9. With Jane and (she, her) came a flock of relatives.

10. Between Silvio and (me, I) there was no agreement.

EXERCISE B Some of the personal pronouns in the following sentences are in the subject form when they should be in the object form. Cross out any incorrect pronoun and write the correct form above it. (Add 4 points for each correctly marked sentence.)

1. Nothing was too difficult for Russell and I.

2. Shelly got along without Ann and I very nicely.

3. The present was delivered to me but was really for he or Dave.

4. We kept the secret among Bernadette, Esther, and I.

5. Below, Clyde and I saw three men in a rowboat.

6. Nicky and she suddenly arrived with both of them.

7. Except for the Russoffs and we, nobody knew the hiding place.

8. Seymour sat down between Mickey and I.

9. Behind Walt and she came a string of cars.

10. Before Kiki and she stood a police officer and I.

11. The cars swung out around Wallace and I and into the road.

12. The Furukawas and they live near Jill and me.

13. Gary and he took a position against him and I.

14. The rain poured down like a waterfall on Rosa, Madeline, and I.

15. The whole argument is beneath Larry and he and I.

16. The Ogilvies and she finally arrived.

17. Like Harry and I, Ida and she do not care much for fishing.

18. With Mavis and I came Hal and he.

19. Dad and he were saving ice cream for Uncle Godfrey and they.

20. Everyone enjoyed the performance, except for Dita Ruiz and I.

21. Concerning Clara and she, I have nothing further to add.

22. Riding in the ski lift were Mandy and she.

23. What could I tell Oliver and they to help explain the mix up?

24. Karen wrote a story about Monica and she.

25. The story was read by Florence and I.

Chapter Review

EXERCISE A   Identify the use of each italicized pronoun by writing above it *subj.* for subject, *s.c.* for subject complement, *d.o.* for direct object, or *o.p.* for object of a preposition. (Add 5 points for each correct answer.)

1   *I* like studying about turtles, but my brother doesn't. Reptiles upset
2   *him. He* doesn't like observing crawling creatures. For *him,* any
3   reptile is repulsive. *I,* on the other hand, find *them* fascinating. The
4   size of some turtles interests *me.* Compared to their extinct relatives,
5   some of *them* seem mere pygmies. One museum displays the skeleton
6   of an extinct turtle. The guide told *us* that *it* must have weighed about
7   6,000 pounds. Nevertheless, *they* still grow very large today. The
8   largest living species consists of the leatherback turtles. It is *they* who
9   achieve sizes up to 1,500 pounds. The plates covering the shells of
10   the hawksbill turtle are used by some of *us* for tortoise shell orna-
11   ments. My mother has a tortoise shell comb that her mother gave
12   to *her. She* finds tortoise shell very beautiful. One day, *I* would like
13   to travel to the Galápagos Islands with my family. *We* could study
14   turtles close up. *I* am sure even my brother would be interested in
15   turtles once *he* saw some of the more remarkable species. If ever
16   there were a born naturalist, it is *I.*

EXERCISE B   Fill the blank in each sentence with the correct one of the two pronouns printed in italics. (Add 5 points for each correct answer.)

he, him   1. Roxanne and . . . . rode horseback this morning.

he, him   2. It was . . . . with whom I saw you at lunch.

They, Them   3. . . . . were the kindest words the child had ever heard.

she, her   4. We were not expecting . . . . and Maxine for breakfast.

I, me   5. On Sunday Dad and . . . . are driving to Eastport.

we, us   6. Except for the Bernaths and . . . ., everyone has moved away.

they, them 7. We visited . . . . and Stephanie White in Butte last summer.

I, me 8. Dr. Hernandez was extremely kind to my sister and . . . .

we, us 9. It was . . . . who wrote that editorial without any help from anyone.

he, him 10. Besides you and . . . . , there will be the Holden twins.

she, her 11. Mike and . . . . often gather driftwood along the beach.

she, her 12. Near . . . . and the bull was a man with a cape.

they, them 13. Could it have been . . . . in the back seat?

we, us 14. They invited the Judsons and . . . . to see their slides.

I, me 15. If it had been Jasper, Dinah, or . . . . , we would have been nervous.

I, me 16. The man grabbed Don and . . . . and pointed to the door.

we, us 17. May the Dobrowskis and . . . . go to the movie now?

they, them 18. We have all suffered from . . . . and their practical jokes.

he, him 19. Did Rusty let you or . . . . try out for the team?

she, her 20. Mr. Bugati thinks it was . . . . who sang the best.

EXERCISE C Cross out any incorrect pronoun and write the correct form above it. (Add 20 points for each correctly marked sentence.)

A. Slowly, the fire crept nearer to Michael and he.

1. Too late, Ossie and me had realized what was the matter.

2. Someone is always making trouble for him and I.

3. Could the two boys in the back row have been they?

4. Her and Carol will notify the other members and they of the meeting.

5. Near Conrad and we stood she and her brother.

Cumulative Review

A Above each italicized word, write its part of speech, using the usual abbreviations: *n.* (noun), *pron.* (pronoun), *adj.* (adjective), *v.* (verb), *adv.* (adverb), *prep.* (preposition). (Add 2 points for each correct answer.)

1   Pia and *I* rebuilt an *old* car *during* the *summer.* It *was* a 1931 Model

2   A Ford. We *stripped* it *down* and *cleaned every* part. *It* was a lot *of*

3   work to get the *old rust* and grease off. *Afterward, we hammered* the

4   *dents* out of the *fenders* and *repainted* the *body.*

In the rest of this paragraph, underline the subject of each sentence once and the verb twice. Circle each complement and write above it the appropriate abbreviation: *d.o.* for direct object, *s.c.* for subject complement.

5   This was actually the easiest part of the job. My sister then found a

6   rebuilt motor for the Ford, and we replaced the window glass and

7   bought a new battery. At last the car ran perfectly. We brought the car

8   to inspection and it passed. Now we can drive around in our car and

9   have become the objects of our friends' admiration. My sister and

10   I have joined an antique car society. Next year we and a friend will

11   restore a vintage Stutz Bearcat.

B The following paragraph contains sentence fragments, run-on sentences, and errors in commas and capitalization. Correct all these mistakes. (Add 4 points for each correct answer.)

1   Simon Bolivar a famous leader of the movement for independence

2   in south America was born in caracas venezuela on July 24 1783. His

3   parents were rich. But died in his childhood. He was educated by

4   tutors, for a while he lived in paris. Later, in Caracas, he and other

5   rebels drafted a venezuelan constitution but the rebels were defeated

6   by the spanish army Bolivar assembled another army, but was again

7   defeated and forced into exile. He finally drove the spanish from

8   Venezuela. After ten years of bitter fighting. He achieved his final

9   victory the battle of Ayacucho peru on december 9 1824.

C The following sentences contain errors in agreement. Cross out any incorrect verb and write the correct verb above it. (Add 10 points for each correct answer.)

1. The boats in the harbor was all damaged by the storm.

2. The trees along the boulevard has all turned color.

3. The brickwork of those old buildings are a beautiful color.

4. Here is two or three new stamps for your collection.

5. It don't really matter whether he comes or not.

6. Everybody in these towns are shooting pheasants out of season.

7. Ted and the boy next door is making a tree house.

8. There stands the drum major and his assistants.

9. Either of the two records sound all right to me.

10. The gall of those people get me down.

D Underline the correct one of the two verb forms given in parentheses. (Add 5 points for each correct answer.)

1. They (saw, seen) both pictures on the same program.

2. The flowers have all (fell, fallen) from the plants.

3. The speaker (lay, laid) the notes aside and began to talk.

4. The front doorbell has been (rang, rung) several times.

5. I have (went, gone) to California three years in a row.

6. The letter was (wrote, written) before I (saw, seen) you.

7. Bernie (sat, set) down and (drank, drunk) three bottles of soda.

8. They (came, come) into the valley last night through the pass.

9. The cat is (laying, lying) under the tree.

10. It's no use (laying, lying) about the plans you have (lain, laid).

11. I have not (begun, began) my homework yet.

12. The winner was (chose, chosen) and (gave, given) the prize.

13. Sharon (brung, brought) the potato salad.

14. *Fifth Chinese Daughter* was (written, wrote) by Jade Snow Wong.

15. The students (sat, set) their pens on their desks.

16. Coretta has (gone, went) out.

Building Vocabulary:
Choosing the Appropriate Word

People who are a little over the average weight might not mind being called *plump* or even *stout,* but they would probably think it rude or unkind if someone told them they were *obese.* All three words are close enough in meaning to be called synonyms. The big difference is not in the meaning but in the feelings that go with these words. In order to use words well, it is not enough to get the meaning right. You must also make sure that the feelings that go with the words are appropriate to what you are trying to say.

Words that are close in meaning may differ greatly in what they suggest.

Compare the following sentences. See if you can work out from the context the meanings of the words in red and the feelings they suggest.

EXAMPLES Mary McLeod Bethune, a founder of Bethune-Cookman College, was one of the **eminent** educators of her day.
Billy the Kid, the **notorious** bandit, died a violent death.

Both *eminent* and *notorious* have the general meaning of "famous or well known for some accomplishment." *Eminent,* however, means "famous for something good," while *notorious* means "famous for something bad." It would be just as mistaken to say that Bethune was a "notorious educator" as to say that Billy the Kid was an "eminent bandit." The feelings which the two words suggest are entirely different.

Study the following pairs of words, noting their similar meanings and the very different feelings that they suggest. Try to think of contexts in which each word would be appropriate.

disagree /dis ə grḗ/, *v.* **wrangle** /ráng gəl/, *v.* Both words mean to have a difference of opinion about something. *Disagree* suggests little feeling and is a good word for plain factual statement. Two friends might *disagree* about something without any bad feeling, but if they have a long, drawn-out, angry argument, unpleasant for them and everyone else, they are *wrangling.*

resolute /réz ə lūt/, *adj.* **pugnacious** /pug nā́ shəs/, *adj.* These words have similarities in meaning, but are not close enough to be true synonyms. Both suggest great strength of purpose, a readi-

ness to stand up for what one thinks right. *Resolute* suggests a good quality, *pugnacious* a quality that is not so good. *Resolute* people have thought out their positions and feel deeply that they are right. *Pugnacious* people are always ready for a fight, though not usually without a good reason.

persistent /pər sís tənt/, *adj.* **obstinate** /ób stə nit/, *adj.* Both words mean sticking to something without giving up. *Persistent* means going on with some activity, carrying it through, if possible, to its conclusion. *Obstinate* suggests a quality that may not be good. An *obsti-*

nate person will stick to an opinion to the point of being annoying about it, even if in the wrong.

aloof /ə lūf/, *adj.* **haughty** /háu tē/, *adj.* Both words suggest excessive pride. *Aloof* people show their feelings of superiority by keeping away from other people. *Haughty* people show pride actively by treating other people with contempt.

tranquil /tráng kwil/, *adj.* **meek** /mēk/, *adj.* Both words suggest a calm, quiet disposition. *Tranquil* is used only with the "good" suggestion of untroubled, at peace with oneself. *Meek* means without anger or envy and strictly speaking is also a "good" word, but it is often used to mean overly submissive or lacking in spirit, too ready to give in to others.

EXERCISE In each blank, write the word from this lesson that makes the best sense. Make sure that the suggested feelings of the word as well as its basic meaning fit the context. (Add 10 points for each correct answer.)

1. Unfortunately, people often take advantage of Waldo's . . . . disposition.

2. Metcalf is so naturally . . . . that he cannot bring himself to join in any school activities.

3. Although I . . . . completely with you, I shall always defend your right to express your views.

4. Only an extremely . . . . person would have had the courage to face the angry mob single-handed and unarmed.

5. It was certain beforehand that two people as . . . . in their opinions as the governor and Mayor Laverty would immediately begin to . . . . over the new city budget.

6. After standing up to so many . . . . people all day long, Mother is glad to return to the . . . . atmosphere of home.

7. Quietly . . . . as always, Lola finally persuaded us.

8. The company's . . . . president kept the salesclerk waiting for two solid hours.

REVIEW EXERCISE In the space to the left of each italicized word, write the letter of the best meaning. (Add 20 points for each correct answer.)

. . . . 1. a *lenient* parent

. . . . 2. a *tactful* remark

. . . . 3. *spontaneous* liking

. . . . 4. *contemplate* an idea

. . . . 5. *shun* an enemy

a. careful about others' feelings

b. to avoid completely

c. not strict or severe

d. to consider deeply

e. without outside cause

190

Spelling: Silent Consonants

One of the results of its long and complicated history is that English contains a number of words that have "silent" or unpronounced consonants. Some English words with silent consonants are taken from Latin, and the Latin spelling does not correspond to the way we now pronounce the words. Among such words of Latin origin are

salmon	debt	solemn
alms	doubt	column

Many other words containing silent consonants are derived from Old English forms in which the consonants *were* pronounced. The word *knot*, for example, was pronounced with the letter *k* sounded as /k/.

Here is a sampling of some modern English words which still retain a silent consonant as a kind of reminder of the days when the English language was Old English and people still sounded these now silent letters.

limb	write	know
climb	sword	knee
Wednesday	half	listen
handsome	folk	soften

EXERCISE A Draw a circle around the silent consonant in each word below. Say the word softly, and consult a dictionary, if necessary. (Add 5 points for each correct answer.)

1. knife	6. rustle	11. wreck	16. knack
2. often	7. mortgage	12. stalk	17. handsome
3. wrinkle	8. handkerchief	13. condemn	18. honest
4. hymn	9. fasten	14. knowledge	19. write
5. thumb	10. subtle	15. raspberry	20. trestle

EXERCISE B Fill in the blanks in each incomplete word below. The meaning of the word is given in parentheses. (Add 20 points for each correct answer.)

1. an . . . . . er (a reply)

2. . . . . . eumonia (a serious lung disease)

3. mu . . . . . le (a bundle of body tissue)

4. . . . . . ist (the joint connecting the hand and the arm)

5. ca . . . . . le (a large building with thick walls)

EXERCISE C The silent consonant (or consonants) in each word below is printed in red. Look at each word carefully. Try to picture it, especially the silent consonant, in your mind. Then be ready to write the words as your teacher dictates them. (Add 10 points for each correct answer.)

1. scene
2. island
3. psalm
4. toward
5. ghost

6. gnaw
7. descend
8. almond
9. wrestle
10. corps

EXERCISE D Review all of the words you have studied in this lesson. Look at the word; close your eyes and picture it; look at it again; write it; check your written word. Concentrate on those words you had trouble with. Now be ready to write all of the words correctly as your teacher dictates them to you. (Add 4 points for each correct answer.)

REVIEW EXERCISE Underline the correct word from each pair in parentheses. (Add 10 points for each correct answer.)

1. My mother's favorite (sent, scent) is musk.
2. All of the bookcases in this room are (stationary, stationery).
3. We had only two hours in which to (altar, alter) the costumes.
4. The pitcher (through, threw) a fast ball.
5. Tim, did you (brake, break) the good news to them yet?
6. Let's all (meet, meat) at the bus stop at eight o'clock.
7. The rescuers could (hear, here) voices from deep inside the cavern.
8. This picture was taken right in front of the (capital, capitol).
9. What are the (principals, principles) of your club?
10. You must rub the paint off with (course, coarse) steel wool.

Apostrophes for Contractions

Whenever you use a word like *don't* (for *do not*) or *I'm* (for *I am*)—as you do very often in conversation—you are using a *contraction*. A contraction is simply two words joined together, with some of the letters left out.

Use an apostrophe to show where letters have been left out in a contraction.

The most commonly contracted words are *is, are, have, not,* and *will.* In the following examples, notice which letters in these words are replaced by the apostrophe.

IS	he's	here's	there's	who's		
ARE	we're	you're	they're			
HAVE	I've	you've	we've	they've		
NOT	isn't	aren't	haven't	don't	doesn't	didn't
	wasn't	weren't	couldn't			
WILL	I'll	you'll	we'll	they'll	who'll	

Are, have, and *will* are usually contracted only with personal pronouns (*we're, I've, she'll*), while *not* combines mainly with helping verbs. *Is* (*'s*), however, may be contracted with almost any noun or pronoun.

EXAMPLES   The work's (= work is) too hard.
Nothing's (= Nothing is) getting done.

Is and *has* both have the same contraction (*'s*). So do *had* and *would* (*'d*). With both pairs of contractions, you must be careful to make clear which word you mean. In writing, it is perhaps best to avoid these contractions simply because they may not always be clear.

EXAMPLES   He's left now = He is left now *or* He has left now
They'd run home = They would run home *or* They had run home

Finally, notice these three contractions, which are a little different from the ones listed above.

EXAMPLES   Let us go = Let's go
They cannot = They can't
She will not = She won't

Standard English usage does not permit any contraction of *am not.* Never use *ain't.* Do not use *aren't* with the pronoun *I.* This is perhaps one of the most common errors in standard English usage. Many of us say "Aren't I?" when we should say "Am I not?" Although this is accept-

195

able in nonstandard usage, we should remember, especially when writing, that the correct form is "Am I not?"

NONSTANDARD   *Aren't* (= are not) I invited? I *ain't* worried.
STANDARD   **Am** I **not** invited? I**'m** (= I am) **not** worried.

EXERCISE A Write the contractions of the following words, putting the apostrophe in place of the omitted letters. (Add 4 points for each correct answer.)

A. you have   ..*you've*...   13. let us   . . . .

 1. did not   . . . .   14. you would   . . . .

 2. I am   . . . .   15. cannot   . . . .

 3. we will   . . . .   16. who will   . . . .

 4. is not   . . . .   17. here is   . . . .

 5. who is   . . . .   18. we have   . . . .

 6. have not   . . . .   19. you are   . . . .

 7. we are   . . . .   20. Glenn is   . . . .

 8. was not   . . . .   21. were not   . . . .

 9. they have   . . . .   22. she will   . . . .

10. will not   . . . .   23. they are   . . . .

11. there is   . . . .   24. it has   . . . .

12. I am not   . . . .   25. you have   . . . .

EXERCISE B The following sentences contain possessive nouns and contractions, but all the apostrophes are missing. Supply the omitted apostrophes. (Add 10 points for each correctly marked sentence.)

A. Wholl take Ambroses place?

 1. Mayas dog wont run out into the street any more.

 2. Lets not go to the bowling match tonight.

 3. Im not happy about the mayors decision.

 4. She wasnt so sure before the teams winning streak.

 5. Theyll use the students dining room.

 6. She shouldnt mark her books that way.

 7. Theyve no reason for complaint.

 8. Dont be so sure that hell win.

 9. Whos going to tell her about Jacks failure?

10. I wont repeat what youve said to me.

196   © 1977 HBJ

Apostrophes: Some DON'TS

1. DON'T confuse the possessive pronouns with the contractions that sound like them.

The personal pronouns have special possessive forms that show possession all by themselves, *without the use of the apostrophe.*

EXAMPLES **His** friends are **ours. Its** habits are like **theirs.**

Some of the possessive pronouns sound just like contractions. *Whose,* which is used in asking questions, also sounds like a contraction. When in doubt, ask yourself whether the word is used as a possessive pronoun or as a contraction (a pronoun plus a verb).

INCORRECT *It's* coat is shaggy.   *Its* time to leave.
CORRECT **Its** (possessive) coat is shaggy.   **It's** (= *it* + *is*) time to leave.

INCORRECT *Their's* looks better.   *Theirs* the answer.
CORRECT **Theirs** (possessive) looks better.   **There's** (= *there* + *is*) the answer.

INCORRECT *Who's* book is that?   *Whose* coming with us?
CORRECT **Whose** (possessive) book is that?   **Who's** (= *who* + *is*) coming with us?

2. DON'T use an apostrophe with plural nouns that do not show ownership.

Some careless people get carried away by apostrophes. They add them to any plural noun, especially one that happens to have a possessive in front of it. An apostrophe stuck in where it is not needed is just as wrong as an apostrophe left out where it really belongs.

INCORRECT The men's *hats'* blew off.
CORRECT The men's **hats** blew off.   (*Hats* is not possessive.)

3. DON'T misplace the apostrophe.

Again through carelessness, people sometimes put the apostrophe at the wrong point in the contraction. Remember that the purpose of the apostrophe is to show where letters are left out. Put the apostrophe only where letters have been omitted.

INCORRECT You *ca'nt* do that again.
CORRECT You **can't** do that again.   (The apostrophe goes in place of *no* in the long form, *cannot.*)

EXERCISE A Underline the correct form of the pair of words in parentheses in the following sentences. (Add 10 points for each correct answer.)

1. (<u>Whose</u>, Who's) book am I using?

2. (Your, <u>You're</u>) right about that stop sign.

3. Stop wiggling (<u>your</u>, you're) feet.

4. (<u>Their</u>, They're) ideas about football are all wrong.

5. (Its, <u>It's</u>) unreasonable of him to expect so much work.

6. (Their, <u>They're</u>) sure that set of tools belongs to them.

7. (<u>Ours</u>, Our's) is a happy class.

8. (Theirs, <u>There's</u>) the one that lost the license plate.

9. (Their, <u>They're</u>) all coming to visit us.

10. (Theirs, <u>There's</u>) no reason for all that racket.

EXERCISE B If the italicized word or contraction is correct, write *C* in the appropriate space to the right. If it is not correct, write the word or contraction correctly in the proper space. (Add 5 points for each correct answer.)

1	"*Don't* you tell me *its* my turn again,"	C	it's
2	Carla insisted. "*I'm* sure *Ive* done it	C	I've
3	two nights running. *Is'nt* that so, Nora?"	Isn't	
4	*Noras' stamps'* held her interest, and	Nora's	stamps
5	she *did'nt* answer. It was *Bill's* problem.	didn't	C
6	"Oh, no," said Bill, "*youve* skipped	you've	
7	twice. *Someone's* got to clean *it's* cage,	C	its
8	but I know it *ain't* my turn."	isn't	
9	"*Who's* hamster is it—*yours,*" Dad	Whose	C
10	asked, "or *Carla's* or *Noras?*"	C	Nora's
11	"*Its their's!*" each shouted at once,	It's	C
12	pointing to the other two.		
13	"Tonight," said Dad, "*its* all *yours,* and	it's	C
14	now *your* all three going to feed it.	you're	

Punctuating Quotations

Compare these two sentences:

The pirate said that I would die for what I had done.
The pirate shouted, "Traitor! You'll walk the plank for this!"

The first sentence tells more or less what the pirate said, in different words. The second sentence gives the pirate's exact words. When you give someone's exact words, you are *quoting* that person, and what you quote is called a *direct quotation—quotation* for short.

Use quotation marks to enclose a direct quotation—a person's exact words.

EXAMPLES "Nothing can change my mind," I told her.
The man replied, "Haven't you said that twice already?"
"How do you spell *psychology?*" asked Norman.

A direct quotation begins with a capital letter.

In other words, a sentence that is quoted begins like any other sentence.

EXAMPLE The officer said, "Let's see your license."

A direct quotation is set off from the rest of the sentence by commas.

EXAMPLES "I'll see you at the game tonight," Homer remarked.
Priscilla inquired, "Do you think it will rain today?"

If a quotation occurs *within* a sentence, it needs two commas—one at the beginning and one at the end. Such a quotation is usually very short.

EXAMPLE Mary said, "We could go to my house," and then was silent.

Notice, in the examples above, how a quotation ends. The comma (period, question mark, or exclamation point) is placed *inside* the closing quotation marks. The comma at the beginning of a quotation, on the other hand, is *outside* the opening quotation mark.

One other comma use comes up mostly, though not only, in direct quotations—the word of direct address. A word of direct address is whatever name or title is used when speaking to a person.

A word of direct address is set off by commas.

EXAMPLES Mr. Hanford asked, "Willy, do you know the answer or not?"
"Please, Senator, give me your autograph," Joyce said.

EXERCISE A Add capital letters, periods, question marks, commas, and quotation marks where they are needed for the direct quotations in the following sentences. Remember to put the beginning comma outside the quotation marks and the closing punctuation mark inside. (Add 10 points for each correctly marked sentence.)

1. "We would like to plant a rooftop garden," Aretha said.

2. "That sounds like a good idea," the superintendent replied.

3. Brenda asked, "Could we use a small section of the roof on the south side?"

4. Aretha added, "We really wouldn't need too much space."

5. "I'm certain something could be arranged," commented the superintendent.

6. Then he added, "What are you planning to grow?"

7. "We were thinking of growing tomatoes, lettuce, radishes, and cucumbers," Aretha replied.

8. Brenda said, "And I was planning on setting aside a tiny section for herbs."

9. "I'll help to block off a small section this afternoon," the superintendent responded.

10. The friends cheerfully replied, "Oh, thank you very much."

EXERCISE B Some of the following sentences need additional punctuation, and some do not. Supply the missing punctuation marks and capital letters. (Add 5 points for each correct answer.)

THE WINNER

1   Arlene asked me, "Why I expected her to win." "I admire your
2   determination," I told her. Then I went on, "It's persistence that
3   counts in sports. But she said, "that she still wasn't convinced. I told
4   her all the things I could think of to cheer her up. And, of course,
5   she won.
6   Afterward, she asked me, "Did you really expect me to win?"
7   She insisted, "that she couldn't believe it," and I retorted, "Don't be so
8   modest champ."
9   She laughed and said, "Well, I can't deny I practiced hard."

200   © 1977 HBJ

Working with Longer Quotations

Both for interest and clarity, you often interrupt a quotation with the words that tell who is talking—*he said, they replied,* and so on. When you interrupt a quotation in this way, you put a comma and quotation marks *after* the first part of the quotation and a comma and quotation marks *before* the second part of the quotation.

EXAMPLES   "We're so near now," he said, "that we ought to be home by eight at the latest."

"Come over here," shouted Mr. Bailey, "and explain what you were doing here!"

Notice that in a divided quotation, the second part of the quoted sentence begins with a small letter.

EXAMPLES   "Do you want to lie down," Gertrude suggested, "until you feel better?"

"I wonder," said Geraldine with a troubled sigh, "whether that will really do me any good."

In telling a story, you often quote the conversation of two or more people. In writing, conversation of this kind is known as *dialogue.*

When you write the conversation of two or more persons, begin a new paragraph each time the speaker changes.

EXAMPLES   "I thought I saw you on Third Street yesterday," John remarked.

"Oh, no," said Susie, "I was out of town, so it must have been some other person."

"Where did you go, Susie?" John continued.

"Well, you see, Aunt Lila's been sick," Susie explained, "and we all drove over to see how she was getting along."

Often, you quote several sentences at a time. You may be reporting conversation, or you may be quoting sentences from a book.

When a quotation consists of more than one sentence, put quotation marks only at the beginning and end of the whole quotation.

INCORRECT   Leon shouted, "Can you still hear me, Jennifer?" "The whole house is going." "The roof will collapse any minute." "Hurry up!"

CORRECT   Leon shouted,   "Can you still hear me, Jennifer? The whole house is going. The roof will collapse any minute. Hurry up!"

Too many quotation marks (in the first example) are confusing. They make the reader think several people are talking instead of just one.

EXERCISE A The commas and quotation marks have been omitted from the following sentences. Put them in. Not every sentence requires punctuation. (Add 10 points for each correctly marked sentence.)

A. "I wonder, Margie," Jenny sighed, "if we really ought to go."

1. Where the director inquired do you find such elegant costumes?

2. "We'll just stay a few minutes Jim I said and then we'll go home."

3. Gloria told Miss Stivik that she feared the worst.

4. "Whenever you talk Toby laughed you sound just like Uncle Pud."

5. "Trust me the scout whispered to get you out of this mess."

6. "In this region said Mr. O'Hare we have gold mines and sheep."

7. Julia said I bet I would have liked traveling in a covered wagon.

8. "Next time says a sign take the train."

9. Marv had sworn to all of us that he was telling the truth.

10. "But as for me shouted Teddy I just like talking to people!"

EXERCISE B Supply the missing punctuation marks in the following dialogue. Use a paragraph sign (¶) to show where the speaker changes and a new paragraph should begin. (Add 4 points for each correct answer.)

1   "Racquel, have you developed the photographs for the school paper
2   yet?" asked Cheryl, "We need them by noon." ¶ "Yes" said
3   Racquel, "I brought them to Mrs. Ieradi's office." ¶ Cheryl inquired,
4   "How did they turn out? Was the lighting good enough? ¶ I had
5   some difficulty with the three shots I took at night," Racquel re-
6   sponded, "but the rest are pretty sharp." ¶ "Thats great!" said
7   Cheryl, "After all our hard work, I almost cant wait to see the first
8   issue of the paper in print."

Chapter Review

EXERCISE A Form the possessives of the following expressions by adding either apostrophe *s* (*'s*) or just an apostrophe ('). (Add 4 points for each correct item.)

1. the sun.... rays
2. the trucks.... tires
3. the men.... hats
4. anyone.... promises
5. the stars.... twinkling
6. the house.... basement
7. the nations.... ambassadors
8. the children.... pets
9. a sick man.... hopes
10. some magazines.... articles
11. the bridge.... maintenance
12. nobody.... fault

Write the contractions of the following expressions, being careful to put the apostrophes in the right places.

13. will not ....
14. did not ....
15. who is ....
16. she will ....
17. cannot ....
18. it has been ....
19. has not ....
20. here is ....
21. could not ....
22. let us ....
23. you would ....
24. I shall ....
25. would not ....

EXERCISE B In the following sentences, *cross out* the word in parentheses that should not be used. (Add 5 points for each correct answer.)

1. (Whose, Who's) coat is this lying on the floor?
2. I think (your, you're) idea of hair styles is better than (theirs, their's).
3. (Its, It's) a pleasure to see you.
4. Afterward, (your, you're) going to cut the grass.
5. (Hers, Her's) was a very poor choice, but (ours, our's) was even worse.
6. (Their, They're) trip starts tomorrow, and (their, they're) going to Nova Scotia.
7. (Your, You're) never going to finish (your, you're) book.
8. I envy that cheerfulness of (hers, her's).
9. (Ours, Our's) is the first house in the block to get one.
10. (Its, It's) hind leg must be hurt.

11. During (their, they're) vacation, (their, they're) leaving the dog behind in a kennel.

12. Their boat lost (its, it's) mast, but (ours, our's) is all right.

13. (Whose, Who's) going to repair (yours, your's) for you?

EXERCISE C Supply quotation marks, commas, and other punctuation marks. (Add 10 points for each correctly marked sentence.)

1. Your resistance to my plan he said is incomprehensible.

2. Im so anxious to get away she said that I can hardly wait.

3. Ms. Beame asked if the answer was right or wrong.

4. Wheres the fire mister asked the officer.

5. Theres an enemy patrol over the ridge Captain said the corporal.

6. What I want to know Mother she said is why are you going?

7. Did the old man really say that to Jerry she asked.

8. Thats an insult you coward he sneered and you don't dare repeat it.

9. Since its my last flight, lets enjoy it said the ace pilot.

10. What chance he asked have you got against such odds?

EXERCISE D Supply the commas, quotation marks, capital letters, and apostrophes needed in the following dialogue. Where a new paragraph should begin, put in the paragraph sign (¶). (Add 2 points for each correct answer.)

DON'T OPEN IT, CHARLOTTE

1 Mom said Charlotte plaintively Im certain I heard a noise like the
2 opening of a spaceships airlock.   Thats a fine idea, Rosalie Pumply
3 replied but I guess were all a little tired tonight.   I think its in the
4 backyard the girl continued.   Thats just fine murmured the girls
5 tired mother. The young girls voice sank to a frightened whisper as
6 she said please, Mom, weve got to do something.   Theyre coming
7 out.   Theyve turned on their ray guns.   Watch out!   Arent you
8 listening Mom?   Whats that youre saying.   Mrs. Pumply in-
9 quired.   How can you read your paper at a time like this?   the girl
10 shouted.   Wearily, Mrs. Pumply said, Of course, but first would
11 you mind seeing whos at our front door?"

Cumulative Review

A In each blank space below, add an appropriate word that will fit into the context of the sentence. Then indicate how each of these words is used by writing above it the appropriate abbreviation: *subj.* for simple subject; *v.* for verb; *s.c.* for subject complement; *d.o.* for direct object; and *o.p.* for object of a preposition. (Add 2 points for each correct answer.)

1. The snowball . . . . him on the . . . .

2. . . . . was almost certainly . . . . in that big black car.

3. The sky above . . . . was a brilliant . . . .

4. Will . . . . of . . . . help . . . . with the dishes?

5. Beyond . . . . and . . . . of empty road.

6. Actually, I rather . . . . a . . . . of their . . . .

7. The chief . . . . of the plot were Alicia and . . . .

8. Has . . . . ever by any . . . . the problem to him?

9. No one . . . . more than Mrs. Fraglin.

10. Black clouds of . . . . blocked his . . . . of them.

B In the following paragraph, correct the capitalization, sentence fragments, and run-on sentences, and supply missing commas. (Add 2 points for each correct answer.)

FIREWORKS!

1 Long before the people of europe knew anything about gun-
2 powder, the chinese had found a variety of uses for it. Chinese rockets
3 were crude inaccurate and dangerous as weapons of war but they
4 produced a splendid bang and a brilliant light. Qualities that are
5 highly desirable in fireworks. Even today fireworks play a leading
6 part. In the celebration of the chinese new year. The United States
7 however is the world's leading consumer of fireworks. The campaign
8 for a "safe and sane" fourth of July has of course eliminated some
9 of the fun along with the danger, however Independence day would
10 simply not be the same to most of us without a public display of
11 fireworks. On the other hand in england and in Hawaii, our forty-

12 ninth State fireworks are traditional. In the celebration of new year's
13 day. French Customs in the use of fireworks are similar to ours, the
14 french use rockets roman candles pinwheels and other devices to
15 celebrate bastille day the commemoration of the start of the French
16 revolution July 14 1789. Editorial writers for the *new york Times* and
17 other newspapers may to be sure wonder whether fireworks were a
18 gift of god or the devil but it seems likely that people throughout
19 the world will continue to enjoy their bold nighttime display for a
20 long time to come. Indeed fireworks displays sponsored by local com-
21 munities draw large crowds and an afternoon picnic followed by an
22 evening spent watching a fireworks display. Seems to be the traditional
23 way of spending independence day.

C The following sentences contain errors in pronoun and verb usage and in subject-verb agreement. Cross out the incorrect words and write the correct forms above. (Add 4 points for each correct answer.)

 1. Her and I seen them coming and wasn't at all pleased.
 2. Bill and her have lain the problem before Corinne and he.
 3. Last night the Moskoffs come over and brought their pictures.
 4. Don't he ever get tired of laying around doing nothing?
 5. There was no blankets for Barry and I, and we begun to worry.
 6. Several of the students give the same answers on yesterday's test.
 7. One of them has always give trouble, but it isn't she.
 8. Lisa and her often goes to the beach and set there for hours.
 9. Every one of us has fell behind this term.
10. They must have knowed when Joel and him torn down the notice.
11. It was she and him who done it, but they don't seem sorry.
12. They have took you and me for a ride and now they have run out.
13. If either of them has wrote, he should have spoken up about it.

Spelling: Review

EXERCISE A Correctly join each prefix (or suffix) and base word. Write the new word in the blank. (Add 10 points for each correct answer.)

1. dis + similar = ...   6. kindly + ness = ...

2. final + ly = ...   7. due + ly = ...

3. mis + spelled = ...   8. angry + ly = ...

4. thin + ness = ...   9. hoarse + ness = ...

5. un + named = ...   10. true + ly = · · · · · · · · · · · · · · ·

EXERCISE B Make a complete, correctly spelled word by writing the prefix *pre–*, *pro–*, or *per–* in the blank. (Add 10 points for each correct answer.)

1. . . . . . .manent   5. . . . . . .cedes   8. . . . . . .serve

2. . . . . . .fessor   6. . . . . . .mote   9. . . . . . .colate

3. . . . . . .dict   7. . . . . . .mit   10. . . . . . .duce

4. . . . . . .nounce

EXERCISE C Make a complete, correctly spelled word by writing *–cle* or *–cal* in the blank. (Add 10 points for each correct answer.)

1. mechani. . . . . .   5. practi. . . . . .   8. obsta. . . . . .

2. parti. . . . . .   6. bicy. . . . . .   9. musi. . . . . .

3. ici. . . . . .   7. arti. . . . . .   10. comi. . . . . .

4. criti. . . . . .

EXERCISE D Correctly complete each word by writing *ie* or *ei* in the blank. (Add 10 points for each correct answer.)

1. perc. . . . . .ve   5. sl. . . . . .gh   8. n. . . . . .ghbor

2. br. . . . . .f   6. rec. . . . . .ve   9. w. . . . . .ght

3. w. . . . . .rd   7. fr. . . . . .nd   10. l. . . . . .sure

4. y. . . . . .ld

EXERCISE E Make each noun plural or change the form of each verb by writing *s* or *es,* whichever is correct, in the blank. (Add 10 points for each correct answer.)

1. cough. . . . . .   3. approach. . . . . .   5. fox. . . . . .

2. waltz. . . . . .   4. brag. . . . . .   6. glass. . . . . .

7. youth . . . . . .   9. accomplish . . . . . .

8. gas . . . . . .   10. church . . . . . .

EXERCISE F Mentally add *-ing* to each word. Write the new word in the blank. (Add 10 points for each correct answer.)

1. prove . . . .   6. dye . . . .

2. die . . . .   7. make . . . .

3. scare . . . .   8. ride . . . .

4. lie . . . .   9. write . . . .

5. promise . . . .   10. dine . . . .

EXERCISE G Underline the correct word from the pair in parentheses. (Add 10 points for each correct answer.)

1. Are you (through, threw) using the computer yet?

2. Let me (altar, alter) the sleeves of that jacket.

3. Aunt Clare sent Jennifer a box of beautiful yellow (stationary, stationery).

4. What is the (capitol, capital) of Alaska?

5. The weavers were making a (coarse, course) linen fabric.

6. He claims that a UFO landed (here, hear).

7. Carnivorous animals are (meet, meat) eaters.

8. This thunderstorm should (break, brake) the hot spell.

9. Our science teacher is studying to be a junior high school (principle, principal).

10. Do you like the (scent, sent) of wet plaster?

EXERCISE H Be prepared to write the following words from dictation. (Add 5 points for each correct answer.)

1. climb   8. wrinkle   15. ready

2. ghost   9. heaven   16. scream

3. knife   10. muscle   17. toward

4. pleasure   11. scene   18. salmon

5. appeal   12. column   19. sword

6. often   13. steak   20. descend

7. teach   14. island

FRAGMENTS AND RUN-ONS The following paragraph contains ten sentence errors—sentence fragments or run-on sentences. Correct these errors by crossing out or adding periods and by crossing out or adding capital letters as needed. (Add 10 points for each corrected sentence.)

THE RISE AND FALL OF THE HUNS

1   The decline of the Roman Empire was hastened by the attacks
2   of the Huns. A tribe of nomads from northern Asia. These fierce
3   and warlike people began to ravage the territory to the east of the
4   Roman frontiers in the fourth century, the tribes who lived there
5   invaded Roman territory for refuge. Under their greatest leader,
6   Attila, the Huns even established a kingdom. Stretching from eastern
7   Europe deep into Asia. The Huns grew rich from plunder, but they
8   never became civilized. At the peak of his power, Attila invaded
9   Europe. And penetrated as far as modern France. In June of the
10 year 451, he fought a battle. Against the Romans and their allies,
11 afterward, Attila led his horde back to eastern Europe, next year he
12 invaded Italy, where he met the Pope in Milan. And called off the
13 invasion. Deciding to attack Constantinople instead. The next spring
14 he was married, and on the following day he was found dead. Either
15 poisoned by his bride or the victim of a stroke. The Hunnish empire
16 then collapsed.

CAPITALIZATION Where a capital letter is omitted, cross out the small letter and write the correct capital letter above it. If a word is capitalized and should not be, merely cross out the incorrect capital. (Add 5 points for each correctly marked sentence.)

1. Last Spring, mayor Forbes opened our centennial celebration.

2. The battle of lexington began the american Revolution.

3. Rachel Carson wrote a book called *silent spring*.

4. The united tube company had its meeting at lake tahoe.

5. Ms. Knightsmith, manager of the australian branch, was there.

6. She showed them some publicity from the *Sydney daily clarion*.

7. At the meeting, uncle Henry talked about plans for a plant in africa.

8. The african market has a great future, according to *time* magazine.

9. Some people belong to Churches, Synagogues, or Mosques, but others prefer to worship god privately in their own fashion.

10. We heard a talk by major Calkins of the United States air force.

11. Mr. Trent, the chief of police, spoke about national crime prevention week.

12. *Modern fiction studies* has printed a review of all of McCullers' fiction.

13. I saw judge Capp's picture in the *evening Call.*

14. Large areas now mohammedan were once christian.

15. The Oxhide Tire company manufactures most of its Tires in a single plant in the middle west.

16. Stonehenge, to the North of the british city of Salisbury, may have been used in the worship of the ancient celtic Gods.

17. Marissa Bergman is a Manager at the Textco manufacturing company.

18. The alliance of performing artists picketed the television show.

19. Sam Spade was a Private Eye in *the Maltese falcon.*

20. Many commuters who work in New York city but have homes in the Suburbs live in new jersey, connecticut, and long island.

SUBJECT-VERB AGREEMENT Cross out any verb that does not agree with its subject and write the correct form above it. (Add 5 points for each correct sentence.)

1. The choice of the delegates are between two candidates.

2. Here comes the two cousins I wanted you to meet.

3. The cartons of food were falling from the truck one by one.

4. Either Wendell or Lucy has a good chance of winning.

5. Everyone in the class are taking the same test.

6. Well, at least a few of the answers are going to be right.

7. A sandwich, a glass of milk, and a cookie makes a rather skimpy lunch.

8. Near the gate stands a boy and his father.

9. Don't he ever get tired of waiting there?

10. They was hardly fair when they made that decision.

11. Is Carmela and Aunt Mia leaving for Los Angeles next week?

12. Several of Abner's friends have seen the movie, too.

13. There in the box lie the money in a heap of old rags.

14. If they don't come soon, one of us are going to regret it.

15. Either of the candidates are equally acceptable to the voters.

16. A few was lost but there's still several to choose from.

17. Doesn't both of them want to help?

18. Do Ned or one of his friends want to come?

19. A few of the members of the gymnastics class wants to learn to do butterflies.

20. Several of the artists in the exhibition has sold some of their paintings.

VERB USAGE In the appropriate spaces, write the missing principal parts of the following verbs. (Add 4 points for each correct answer.)

PRESENT	SIMPLE PAST	PAST PARTICIPLE
1. drink	. . . .	. . . .
2. ring	. . . .	. . . .
3. choose	. . . .	. . . .
4. freeze	. . . .	. . . .
5. drive	. . . .	. . . .
6. ride	. . . .	. . . .
7. speak	. . . .	. . . .
8. write	. . . .	. . . .

Underline the correct one of the two verb forms in parentheses.

9. We (saw, seen) them when they first (came, come) here.

10. When Jill had (did, done) the work, she (took, taken) it to the study and (lain, laid) it on the desk.

11. The cow has (went, gone) into the cornfield again.

12. Ethel had (tore, torn) her coat as she (ran, run) for the bus.

13. If I'd (knowed, known) you were in a hurry, I'd have brought the book back more promptly.

PRONOUN USAGE In the following sentences, underline the correct form of the pronoun given in parentheses. (Add 10 points for each correct answer.)

1. The person at the foot of the stairs was (she, her).

2. The twins and (he, him) have made all the plans.

3. (He, Him) and (we, us) are in agreement.

4. They will almost certainly give the jobs to George and (he, him).

5. I have asked Mr. Hunter and (he, him) about the matter.

6. The book was written by Dr. Miles in collaboration with Mr. Rawls, Mrs. Lucas, and (he, him).

7. Sandra and (she, her) were the basketball team's cocaptains.

8. Between you and (I, me), Pat knows who did it.

9. Pieces of flying glass cut both Geraldine and (she, her).

APOSTROPHES AND QUOTATION MARKS Supply the missing quotation marks, commas, and apostrophes in the following dialogue. Where the improper word is used, cross it out and write the correct word above. Use the paragraph sign (¶) to show where the speaker changes and a new paragraph should begin. (Add 2 points for each correct answer.)

TO THE MOVIES

1　"Mac old buddy said Casper brightly howd you like to see that
2　show at the Palace tonight?　Whats in it for you, Casper Mac
3　cautiously asked.　Looking slightly hurt, Casper said Gosh, Mac
4　I thought youd enjoy seeing *A Martians Revenge* with me.　Its got
5　Vaughan Tender in it.　Wouldnt it be fun to go together?"　"Youre
6　making it sound pretty good, Mac admitted, "but how are we going
7　to get to the Palace?　That very thought had occurred to me," said
8　Casper smoothly and I thought of your generous brothers car."
9　All right, said Mac with a weary sigh after Jim drives us downtown,
10　whose going to pay for the show?　Casper went on briskly Im just
11　coming to that. Who's money should we borrow this time, Jim's or
12　your's?　Where, asked Mac would a boys money go if it werent
13　for his friends?"

CHAPTER TWELVE

Background for Writing

You have many occasions for writing. You write themes and you write answers on tests. You write letters to friends and relatives. Do you enjoy all the writing that you do, or is it just so much drudgery to you? As with most things, the better you write, the more you are likely to enjoy it. Writing well gives the same kind of satisfaction that you get from making anything the way you want it—a handsome piece of furniture, for example, or a delicious cake.

In this chapter, you shall work through some of the basic writing skills that expert writers use in their own writing. Step by step, you shall learn how to write effective compositions—compositions that say what you really mean, in ways that will be clear and understandable to the reader. As you will see, all the grammar tools that you work with in the first part of this WORKSHOP go into the writing of effective compositions.

LESSON 103

What Is a Paragraph?

The material you have just read at the top of this page is divided into two paragraphs. Notice that the first line of each paragraph is indented a few spaces from the left margin. This paragraph indentation was put there as a signal to you, the reader. When you see a paragraph indentation, you know that the writer has finished with one idea and is about to introduce a new topic.

A paragraph is a series of sentences developing one topic.

That word *one* is important. A good paragraph presents just *one* main idea, or topic, not several. The paragraph which follows below is a poor one precisely because it contains too many different ideas, each of which might be developed in a separate paragraph. In the first sentence, the paragraph seems to be starting out to tell how the books are arranged in the school library, but then, like a badly confused horseback rider, it goes off in all directions at once.

THE BOOKS IN OUR LIBRARY

The books in the school library are arranged by subject. Some public libraries in large cities have many branches. In the little town in Arizona where my aunt lives, there is no public library at all. Once a week, a truck called a bookmobile arrives from Phoenix, loaded with books. In the summers, my aunt comes home to Milwaukee, where she grew up.

A good paragraph presents one topic and *develops* the topic. It takes several steps to develop a roll of film, and it also takes several sentences to develop an idea.

None of these one-sentence "paragraphs" in the following example is really a paragraph at all—none says enough to *develop* an idea. (Notice, however, that the second, third, and fourth sentences all help to explain, or develop, the idea presented in the first sentence. Put together in one paragraph, the four sentences would make an acceptable paragraph.)

USING COLOR EFFECTIVELY

When you decorate a room, it is advisable to plan the color scheme carefully in advance.

A chair covered in purple is not likely to look like much beside that bright green couch that seemed so handsome by itself.

On the other hand, too many browns or grays make a room lifeless and uninteresting, even though they all go well together.

The colors that you choose for your room should fit well together, but they should also have enough variety to give life and interest.

The topic of a paragraph is stated in one sentence in the paragraph. This sentence is called the topic sentence.

The topic sentence is one of the signs of a well-written, well-organized paragraph. Usually the topic sentence is placed first in a paragraph so that the reader will know at once what idea the paragraph is going to present. The topic sentence in the following short paragraph is printed in red. Notice how the remaining sentences help to explain this main idea.

DAWN

Dawn comes slowly over the ocean. At first, while it is still night, the sky and sea are both equally dark. Then gradually the sky becomes transparent, as if the gray light were leaking through a sieve, but the sea remains as dark as night. As light fills the sky, the waves begin to sparkle. At last you see the sun rising over the rim of water, slow, majestic, and bright. A new day has dawned.

EXERCISE A   In each of the following paragraphs, the topic sentence is in italics. Among the other sentences in each paragraph is one which does not belong there. Find and underline the sentence that has nothing to do with the topic sentence.

1. *Automobile racing officially began in 1906 with the first Grand Prix race held by the Automobile Club of France.* Within a short period of time,

the sport became so popular that other countries in Europe instituted their own Grand Prix races. Another internationally popular sport is skiing. The principal teams competing in Grand Prix races were usually owned by large, established automobile companies. Among these were the Alfa Romeo team and the Mercedes-Benz team. The Ferrari team was one of the few independently owned teams. Today, Grand Prix teams tend to be smaller and more independent of automobile companies.

2. *The general direction of weather movement is from west to east.* New Yorkers can be reasonably sure that the weather in Chicago today will have moved on to the East Coast by tomorrow. The change is not always in a straight line, of course. Since many weather systems rotate, winds from the north or the south may cause considerable changes. It often gets very hot in Texas. Nevertheless, New Yorkers may be sure that the weather over Europe is of less interest than the weather over North Dakota.

3. *Reading can be a profitable occupation, or it can be a waste of time.* We can read for pleasure and derive a lively sense of reward from our book. Or we can read merely to escape from the world, in which case we are likely neither to enjoy what we read nor to forget successfully the world around us. Under such circumstances a book becomes nothing but an inferior drug. Many new drugs have appeared on the market in recent years.

4. *Perhaps the most frustrating aspect of a bureaucracy is the slowness with which it operates.* People living in the modern world are the victims of frustration in many forms. When every activity undertaken must be approved by five different people, and all forms filled out in quintuplicate, to be filed with the proper authority, it is no wonder that things get done slowly, if at all. People who yearn for quick action, and see that quick action is quite possible, can be driven nearly frantic by the slow pace of an overorganized system.

EXERCISE B In paragraph 1, find and underline the topic sentence. Read paragraphs 2 and 3 carefully and then, in the space provided, write a suitable topic sentence for each. Remember that the topic sentence should state the topic, or main idea, developed in the paragraph.

1. It was a remote and beautiful island. Two hundred miles south and east lay Tahiti, from which the steamer came once a month with supplies and mail. Out of the South Pacific, the island rose straight and high, like a castle, and its cliffs were draped with waterfalls like lace. On the crags, you saw wild goats and in the forest the small pigs that furnished most of the island's meat.

2. . . . .

The old-fashioned diving suit, with its great weight and its attached air and safety lines, severely limited the exploring that divers could do under water. Today, however, equipped only with an aqualung and a pair of flippers on their feet, adventurous divers can move freely at depths as great as 200 feet. With a submarinelike device called a bathyscaphe, people have descended nearly three miles, to the deepest underwater regions known on earth.

3. . . . .

The grizzly is the only other meat-eating animal that approaches the size of the giant Alaska brown bear, and even the grizzly is not as big. The brown bear's claw marks have been measured fourteen feet up a tree, high enough to reach into your second-story bedroom window if you had annoyed the bear. Its neck alone may be five feet around. A full-grown male weighs close to 1,200 pounds, and a few specimens have been taken that weighed nearly a ton.

WRITING PROJECT Develop one of the following topic sentences into a paragraph. If none of these topics appeals to you, you may choose another of your own. Give your paragraph a suitable title—one like the titles for the paragraphs in this lesson that will tell your readers clearly what your paragraph is going to be about and perhaps arouse their interest in it as well.

1. The seasons in our part of the country are not like those in other regions.
2. The buildings in our town show a variety of styles of architecture.
3. The things people collect often give clues to their character.
4. Some people are sure of what they want to do in life from earliest childhood.
5. Young people ought to be given more interesting work around the home than they ordinarily are.
6. Old-fashioned houses were much more comfortable than modern houses.

Choosing a Subject

To write a satisfactory paragraph or a composition of any length, you must first choose a subject in which you are interested and about which you know something, either from firsthand experience or from information gained through reading, TV, etc. Otherwise, your chances of producing a satisfactory piece of writing are slight. What, for example, do you think is the matter with this paragraph?

Baseball has a long history. It has been a popular game for over sixty years, and during that time there have been important changes in the rules of the game. Crowds have grown larger. More cities have major league teams now than ever before. Houston has the Astrodome, a stadium with a roof. During the past sixty years there have been many great players. They have been noted for different ways of playing the game. Some of them have set records which have stood for many years.

This paragraph is very dull because the writer has offered only a series of general statements, none of which tell readers anything they did not already know. There are no specific details. The subject is too large to treat in one paragraph. Each sentence could become the topic for a paragraph or even for a longer composition. When you write anything you expect others to read, remember that readers expect something from you. It may be information, a fresh viewpoint, or even entertainment. Make your interest contagious. Almost any subject can be made interesting to others if you are interested in it yourself.

1. Choose a subject about which you have something to say from first-hand knowledge or experience.

Here are a few very general subjects, each of which might yield many good subjects for a paragraph. In how many of these areas do you have some special interest? The answer may surprise you!

GENERAL SUBJECTS hobbies cooking fashions history art
literature music mythology sports travel

All of these subjects are, of course, too big, too general, for a short composition. Within each subject, however, you can find many smaller subjects about which you may have the kind of knowledge and experience that will enable you to write an interesting and informative paragraph. For example, do you ski or go trout-fishing or collect all-time baseball records? Do you play a musical instrument? Have you visited one of the historic battlefields of the American Revolution or the War Between the States? When you ask yourself questions like these about any general subject, you are taking the next big step in planning a composition.

2. **Narrow your subject down so that it can be treated adequately within the limits of your composition.**

When your readers finish reading something that you have written, they want to feel that you have covered the main parts of your subject. They should not be left with the feeling that you have overlooked some important part. In planning a paragraph, you need to find a subject that can be properly developed in four or five main sentences.

Suppose, for example, that you are planning a paragraph about hobbies. This large, general subject contains many narrower subjects that might be suitable for a paragraph. By asking yourself questions, you can trim the large subject down to the right size.

1. What hobbies have I had experience with?
2. What one hobby do I know most about?
3. What was my most successful hobby project?

With each question, you narrow down your subject until finally you reach one that you could present adequately within a paragraph. Because you will write from your own special knowledge and experience, you have a good chance of holding your readers' interest and telling them some things they may not have known before—of keeping your end of the writer-reader bargain.

GENERAL SUBJECT	hobbies
NARROWER SUBJECTS	photography model-making gardening stamp collecting
STILL NARROWER	train models ship models model airplanes
NARROWED DOWN	building a model schooner

Here is the one-paragraph composition that might be written on this narrowed-down subject. Notice the italicized topic sentence, which states the main point that the paragraph is going to make about its subject.

BUILDING A MODEL SCHOONER

Using a plastic model kit, you can build a realistic scale model of one of the classic American schooners, perhaps even the America *itself.* The kit will provide all the main parts of the ship, a detailed diagram for assembling them, and the special cement needed to hold the plastic parts together. You will furnish thread for the rigging, model paint, and the patient hours of enjoyment that will be needed to build your model. You will have to follow the diagram to the last detail. For the beginner, the nine sails, ranging from the big and billowing mainsail on the mainmast to the little fore gaff topsail on the foremast, may be a problem. Rigging the ship—putting on the yards of thread that represent the ropes and cables of the original schooner—also requires nimble fingers. When the last tiny knot is tied, however, and the ship is painted to your taste, you will have a handsome and satisfying trophy for your efforts. In the process you will have learned a surprising lot about one of the great sailing ships.

EXERCISE A In each of the following sets of subjects, all but one are too broad to be treated in a single paragraph. Check the one subject in each group that you think might be a good one for a paragraph. Be ready to discuss your reasons for choosing it.

1.

.... A. The first transatlantic TV broadcast

.... B. A history of TV

.... C. The American broadcasting industry today

2.

.... A. Making a motion picture

.... B. A movie star's rise and fall

.... C. Hollywood's brightest new star today

.... D. How television has affected the motion-picture industry

3.

.... A. The smaller animals of North America

.... B. A chipmunk's nest

.... C. American rodents

.... D. Varieties of squirrels in this area

4.

.... A. The benefits of sports

.... B. Learning to swim

.... C. Our little league team's best game

5.

.... A. Folk singers of today

.... B. Building a record collection

.... C. The instruments of jazz

6.

.... A. The purpose of a school newspaper

.... B. Extracurricular school activities

.... C. Getting the most out of school

.... D. Organizing a school glee club

.... E. Our school sports program

7.

.... A. The modern Olympic Games

.... B. Winter sports

.... C. How the American ski team is chosen

.... D. Olympic record holders

8.

.... A. Cities of Europe

.... B. The European capital I would most like to visit

.... C. Career opportunities in the field of travel and transportation

EXERCISE B For each of the following general subjects, list three narrowed-down subjects that would be suitable for a one-paragraph composition. Compare your lists with those of your classmates and see if they agree with your choices.

Family activities: 1. .... 2. ....
.... 3. ....

City activities: 1. .... 2. ....
.... 3. ....

Musical instruments: 1. .... 2. ....
.... 3. ....

Reading for pleasure: 1. .... 2. ....
.... 3. ....

History of transportation: 1. .... 2. ....
.... 3. ....

WRITING PROJECT Choose one of the suitable paragraph topics from Exercise B and develop it into a paragraph. If none of the topics interests you, choose another one. Make sure it is a subject you are ready to write about, and one that is not too big for a paragraph. Begin your paragraph with an effective topic sentence, and make each sentence say something definite about the subject.

Selecting Your Ideas

You are now acquainted with the importance of choosing the subject for a paragraph and then narrowing it down. If the subject was carefully chosen, you will probably know a good deal about it and can easily find any additional facts you may need. In fact, you will probably have more information than you can fit into a single paragraph. How do you sort out the necessary information for the paragraph? First, decide what the *purpose* of your paragraph will be, and then you can decide which points or facts will best help you express that purpose to your readers.

Decide on the purpose of your paragraph.
Make notes on the points you want to cover in your paragraph.

When you have determined your purpose, jot down a few brief notes on the ideas you have. This will help you spot points that do not belong in your paragraph because they are not part of the purpose, or main idea, that you want to develop. Since the notes are for your own use, they can be brief, sometimes just a word or two for a point.

If, for example, you are planning to describe an acting class at the local center, you might list points like these in your notes.

1. location of class
2. time of class
3. teacher's name
4. teacher's background
5. size of class
6. background of students
7. class activities
8. sensory exercises

All these notes are part of your knowledge of the class, and they could be part of a description of the class. However, if you are limiting your composition to one paragraph, you cannot possibly include all of them. You must eliminate those points that are not essential to your purpose. For example, if your purpose is to describe what goes on during an actual class, you would concentrate on points 7 and 8.

Sometimes, the ideas you jot down may cause you to change your purpose. You may even find it better to jot down the ideas about your topic *before* you have clearly determined your purpose. If you do, you may find that the ideas themselves will suggest a purpose to you.

In writing about the class, your purpose may be to *inform* your readers, giving them important facts. Or it might be to get your readers to *share your feeling and ideas* about the class.

Your purpose in writing determines your choice of points to cover and the emphasis you will give to each. Your enjoyment of certain activities, for example, might not be important in an informative account of the class, but it could have a lot to do with how you feel about the class.

Let's suppose that you are writing a one-paragraph description of the class. Your purpose is to give essential information to readers who have little or no knowledge of the class and your personal feeling will not be so important. For this purpose, the list of facts that you already have is about right—minus points 7 and 8.

Here is a paragraph written with the purpose of giving information. Notice that the first few sentences arouse the readers' interest, the topic sentence occurs near the beginning of the paragraph, and the rest of the sentences follow in a logical order.

ACTING AT THE CENTER

Have you wanted to play Long John Silver? Was the role of Eliza Dolittle written just for you? Would you be perfect for a part in *Our Town?* Well, aspiring actors take note. *The local youth center offers a class in acting techniques for teenagers on Saturday afternoons.* The class is taught by Glenda Perkins, a director who has had shows both on and off Broadway. Ms. Perkins has studied with Lee Strasberg at the Actor's Studio in New York and she emphasizes method acting in her classes. In order to ensure that each student will receive individual attention, the classes are limited to fifteen students. Ms. Perkins has said that prospective students do not need any previous experience. In fact, she prefers to train them from scratch.

With a different purpose, you might use the same basic points as the paragraph above, but they would not have the same importance. Suppose, for example, that your main purpose is to arouse interest in the class. Most of the facts about the class would still be there, but the emphasis would be different in order to create the feeling of excitement for your readers.

ACTING AT THE CENTER

It is Saturday, early afternoon. A group of teenagers sit on a bare stage. Their eyes are closed. The lights are dim. The voice of Glenda Perkins drones softly in the background. All attention is focused on the voice. She creates a scene—a beach in May. The young actors are to remember such a scene from their own experiences. They are to recall not only the setting, but the way they felt at the time. They are to come in contact with their feelings. *Yes, method acting has come to the youth center.*

Notice that in this paragraph the italicized sentence at the end gives the main idea and serves as a topic sentence. The writer holds off the main point in order to arouse the readers' interest and hold their attention.

EXERCISE Listed below are six topics suitable for one-paragraph compositions. Each is followed by a list of points that might be used in

222

developing the topic, but one of these points is less important or less closely related than the others and should be omitted. Read each group carefully and decide which point to omit. Place a check in the space to the left of the point that should be dropped.

1. How to be a good baby-sitter

.... A. Take along something to do

.... B. Don't eat or use anything without permission

.... C. Check the baby from time to time to make sure it is sleeping

.... D. How much fun it is to telephone friends!

.... E. If you use the television, keep the volume down

2. Taking care of a pet

.... A. The kind of food it needs

.... B. What animals make good pets

.... C. How often it should be fed

.... D. How often the pet needs to be cleaned

3. Training to be a gymnast

.... A. Disciplining the body through exercise

.... B. Famous gymnasts

.... C. Eating a proper diet

.... D. Developing new skills slowly

.... E. Working out on the parallel bars

4. Improving your stamp collection

.... A. Knowing which stamps are most valuable

.... B. Knowing people to trade with

.... C. Learning about the printing of stamps

.... D. Specializing in the stamps of one country

5. First steps in skiing

.... A. Reading about champion skiers

.... B. Getting the feel of wearing skis

.... C. Controlling your movements

.... D. Choosing the right equipment

.... E. Learning the herringbone

6. Our city's recreation facilities

.... A. Parks and bridle paths

.... B. Beaches and swimming pools

.... C. Stadiums and sports arenas

.... D. Concert halls, auditoriums, and theaters

.... E. Bus terminals, train stations, and airports

WRITING PROJECT Choose one of the topics above and develop it into a paragraph. Before you begin to write, decide whether your purpose will be to give information about your topic or to help your readers to share your feelings or ideas about the topic. Add points or drop them from the list in accordance with your purpose. When you have finished the paragraph, give it a title that will arouse your readers' interest.

If none of the topics in the exercise appeals to you, choose one of your own, or one from the following list, and work out your paragraph in accordance with the suggestions given in this lesson.

PARAGRAPH TOPICS

1. Foreign foods I have liked
2. An unusual pet
3. A secret ambition
4. My favorite comic strip
5. Learning to ride a horse
6. Building a cabinet
7. My favorite rock group
8. Playing a guitar
9. Why I like camping
10. I'm glad I'm a Scorpio (Cancer, Aquarius, etc.).

Making a Good Beginning

How a paragraph begins is important. You cannot force your readers to read what you have written. You must persuade them by showing them right at the beginning that there is some reason for them to go on. For this reason, the beginnings of paragraphs are worth a little extra attention on your part, and the same thing is even more true of longer compositions.

How can you persuade readers to go on with your paragraph? Very often, the best way of doing this is simply to tell them in the first sentence what your topic is going to be. This is why many paragraphs, and particularly those meant to inform, begin with the topic sentence, which sums up the topic of the paragraph.

When the purpose of your paragraph is to inform, the topic sentence often makes the strongest paragraph opening.

EXAMPLES   One day, high-frequency sound waves may be used to perform many common household tasks.
Modern rockets are based on principles of jet propulsion discovered by the Chinese more than a thousand years ago.
What are considered good manners in one country may be bad manners in another.

Quite often, the topic sentence reveals the writer's attitude—or purpose in writing—as well as the topic. If your topic sentence shows that you are strongly against something that the readers are strongly in favor of, they may read no farther. On the other hand, a challenging topic sentence may arouse readers to go on, if only so that they can prove that you are wrong.

EXAMPLES   Over the years, our school's athletic program has been destroyed, bit by bit, by the indifference of the students and the penny-pinching of the school board.
The so-called sport of boxing, which has improved little since the days of the Romans, should be prohibited by law.

The following paragraph opens with the topic sentence, which is printed in italics. Notice the two jobs which the topic sentence does here: it provides a forecast of the subject matter (Western clothing); and it reveals the author's attitude toward it (Western clothing is practical).

Every piece of clothing worn by the cowboy of the old West had a thoroughly practical purpose. The heavy silk bandanna which he wore around his neck, for example, was not simply for decoration. It could be used as a dust mask, a blindfold for a calf, a towel, or a bandage—and it often was. The cowboy's shirt was of cotton and his trousers of heavy denim or some other tough material. His boots were knee-high, and the heavy leather leggings that he wore over them served to protect his legs from thorns or rope burns. Spurs at the heels and a revolver on the hip completed the costume.

Not every paragraph, of course, begins with a topic sentence. There are a number of other paragraph openings that can be very effective in stirring up the readers' interest and persuading them to go on.

EFFECTIVE PARAGRAPH OPENINGS

1. Ask a question to which readers will want to know the answer.
2. Give an example that will lead into your topic.
3. Begin with a well-known quotation.
4. Tell a small incident that will illustrate your topic.
5. Start out with a bit of appropriate dialogue.

The examples that follow illustrate each of these five methods of beginning a paragraph. Notice that the topic sentence, italicized, must now come at a later point in the paragraph. Notice too that in each case the wording of the topic sentence is changed a little from the original topic sentence above so as to fit it more smoothly to the new paragraph opening. The meaning, however, remains the same.

1. Did anyone ever dress more distinctively than the old American cowboy? *His clothing showed him at once for what he was, and so admired are his virtues that his costume is imitated to this day by people who seldom see a cow except from an automobile.* The cowboy wore a silk bandanna. . . .

2. The cowboy provides us with an example of a man whose clothing fitted his work. *Everything he wore had some practical use in his rough, heavy work.* His bandanna, for instance, could be used as a dust mask, or as a blindfold for a calf. . . .

3. "I see by your outfit that you are a cowboy," the old song goes, and *it is true that no person was ever more suitably dressed for work than the old American cowboy.* Around his neck. . . .

4. A man stood silently listening to footsteps approaching him around a corner. He could hear the steps clearly, because with each one came a jingle of spurs. He could tell without seeing the walker that the man approaching was a cowboy—a cowboy dressed for work, with spurs at his bootheels. *No man's clothing ever told more clearly what his job was than the dress of the old American cowboy.* He wore. . . .

5. "Lend me your neckerchief, Slim. I want to blindfold this calf, and mine's already on the one I just roped." One line of conversation, without further explanation, tells us what kind of person was talking, what he did,

where he lived, and how he dressed. He was a cowboy in the old American West, and he dressed for his occupation as distinctively as any person in history. The bandanna alone gives the story away—the bandanna that served as a blindfold or as a dust mask or a towel. *The cowboy's clothing was above all practical. . . .*

In each of these examples, the topic sentence was moved a little farther down in the paragraph. Sometimes it is even postponed clear to the end of the paragraph. Then it serves as a reminder of the material that has just been presented and leaves readers with the basic idea that the writer has been aiming at.

He wore a silk bandanna around his neck which he used as a towel or as a blindfold for a roped calf or as a dust mask in dry weather. His shirt and trousers were of heavy, durable material, and his legs were covered with leggings, to protect him from thorns or rope burns or the hairy hide of an animal he might brush against. He was the old American cowboy, and his dress was practical above all. *In fact, no person could ever be more readily identified by the clothes worn than the cowboy.*

EXERCISE   The topic sentence in each of the following paragraphs is printed in italics. In the space that follows each paragraph, write a new opening for the paragraph, using one of the openings illustrated in this lesson—a question, an example, a quotation, an incident, or a snatch of dialogue. Say what kind of opening you have used. Do not use the same kind of opening twice.

1. *Cats are the natural enemies of bird-lovers.*   Almost any cat, no matter how tame it is at home, will stalk and kill birds if given the opportunity. Birds know this, and they shun a lawn where cats can be found. A family that enjoys watching birds must take steps to keep cats away, or it will see no birds.

New opening: . . . .

. . . .

. . . .

. . . . *Kind of opening:* . . . .

2. *Being thrown by a horse is no trifling matter.*   It commonly leads to broken bones, and serious bruises are the least a thrown rider can expect. And because a horse is only an animal, there is almost no way its rider can anticipate everything that might make the horse shy. A sudden noise, a passing motorcycle, a bird starting up from the underbrush—all these can frighten the most placid mare. A good seat and firm hands are the rider's best protection.

New opening: . . . .

....

....

.... *Kind of opening:* ....

3. *Experiment can lead to disaster, even in the kitchen.* A cake thrown together without a recipe is no cake. Who knows what it is? Foolhardy cooks who invent a cake as they go along may find themselves with nothing more than an exceedingly dirty oven or wall to clean after the explosion, and if they are lucky enough to achieve something that pleases the eye, they have no assurance that the taste will be judged as favorably.

New opening: ....

....

....

.... *Kind of opening:* ....

4. *Riding the subway can be a frustrating experience.* At times the cars are so crowded that you stand no chance of getting a seat. In fact, that's just what you do—stand. The straps to hang on to are almost impossible to reach, especially if you are not above average height. Holding on doesn't really matter though. During rush hours, the trains are so tightly packed that you couldn't possibly fall down. Indeed, by the time you get where you are going in the morning, you are often so tired you just want to go home. But you don't. That would mean you would have to get back on the subway.

New opening: ....

....

....

.... *Kind of opening:* ....

WRITING PROJECT Take one of the openings you have written for the exercise and finish the paragraph in the spirit of the opening. Feel free to vary the material to suit your fancy. Be sure, however, that you have a topic sentence some place in the course of your paragraph.

228

Backing Up Your Ideas

When you have chosen the topic for a paragraph and limited your topic to the right number of points, you are ready to begin writing. The idea that you want to write about may be true and important, but that, by itself, is not enough. You must present your idea in such a way that your readers can see its truth and importance for themselves. When your purpose is to give information or to persuade someone to accept your viewpoint, there are three main ways of backing up your ideas.

Support your ideas by giving facts, reasons, and examples.

Suppose you are writing about opportunities for hiking trips near your home. You might support your main idea—that hikers should be cautious in the woods—with these points.

FACTS	Even near towns, there are large, uninhabited areas.
	Rattlesnakes are still quite numerous in the wooded country.
REASONS	Inexperienced hikers can easily get lost.
	Snakes are all the more dangerous when we do not expect to encounter them.
EXAMPLES	Recently two girls were lost in the woods for a week only twenty miles from your home.
	You yourself were nearly bitten by a rattlesnake.

You could use some or all of these points in a paragraph, depending on just what you were trying to say and whom you were saying it to. Obviously, however, you would not present your points in just this order—first two facts, then two reasons, then two examples. You would arrange the details that support your idea so that readers will see how they fit together and get from them the idea you want them to get.

Arrange supporting details in the order that will be most effective for your purpose.

What is the most effective order? From the standpoint of holding the readers' interest, arranging the details of a paragraph in the *order of importance* is often the best way. Then the paragraph leads up to the most important or most striking fact or reason or example. Because this comes near the end of the paragraph, readers are likely to remember it better than the other details given. If you were writing a paragraph with the details given above, you would probably mention first the danger of getting lost, then other possible dangers such as sunburn and bad water. You would lead up to the most striking danger, snakebite, with your personal experience as an example.

GOOD SENSE FOR HIKERS

Topic Sentence 　1. *Even in our densely populated state, the woods can be dan-*
Reason *gerous for the unwary or the inexperienced.* 　2. In some areas only a few miles from a large town, hikers can be almost as remote from civilization as in the deepest African jungle.
Example 　3. Only last year, two girls wandered off from the trail and were hopelessly lost for a week, even though they were never more
Reason than ten miles from the nearest town. 　4. Water, too, can be
Fact dangerous for thirsty hikers. 　5. Most streams in our state are pure, but any that run through a dairy farm are likely to be polluted and should be drunk only after being boiled or purified
Fact with chlorine tablets. 　6. As the number of farms in the state
Reason decreases, poisonous snakes become more numerous. 　7. For hikers on our local trails, rattlesnakes are all the more dangerous
Example just because they do not expect them. 　8. Last summer, for example, I had a close call myself for just this reason. 　9. I had climbed to the top of a cliff and was enjoying the view when I heard a strange buzzing sound. 　10. I had no idea what the sound could be until I looked around and saw a rattlesnake not six feet away—poised to strike! 　11. For a minute I froze and
Concluding then got away fast. 　12. In our tame and civilized state, the
Statement woods can still reach out and set a trap for hikers who do not treat them with caution and respect.

Notice that the paragraph gives three reasons in support of the topic sentences (sentences 2, 4, and 7). These reasons are, in turn, backed up by facts—statements that can be proved or disproved by evidence (sentences 5 and 6)—and examples (sentences 3 and 8–11, which tell a small incident). Notice particularly the concluding sentence 12, which restates the topic in a forceful way.

Time order is another effective way of organizing the details in a paragraph. This is the order in which we tell a story—what happened first, second, and so on. It is also the order in which we would usually explain how to do something—bake a cake or make a marionette or paint a picture. For example, you could make much the same basic point as the paragraph above by means of a single striking example—by telling, more fully and in time order, the incident of the snake.

DANGER IN THE WOODS

Topic 　1. *The woods of our state still hold some of the excitement that*
Sentence *the earliest settlers found in them, and that, I suppose, is part of*
The Story *their attraction today.* 　2. Last summer, Lydia Turner and I had
Begins gone with my parents to the Pequot State Forest for a picnic.

3. After lunch, Lydia and I went for a walk along one of the trails. 4. My parents had warned us, of course, not to get off the trail, but we were feeling adventurous, and in a little while we had wandered off. 5. We came to a rock ledge and decided to climb it. 6. At the top, we were above the trees and could see the lazy windings of the Algonquin River for miles in both directions. 7. Suddenly, we heard a strange, loud, buzzing sound, and we both froze. 8. "What is it?" Lydia asked in a scared whisper, but I had no more idea than she did. 9. Cautiously, we looked around and saw a large rattlesnake only a few feet off, coiled to strike. 10. Holding our breath, we inched our way back to the edge, slipped over, and tumbled back down **Concluding** to the trail. 11. We had run into just a little more of an adven- **Statement** ture than we knew how to cope with, and we were both thankful to get out of it.

EXERCISE A Each of the groups of sentences below contains three ideas that might be used in a paragraph, but the ideas are not arranged in order. Indicate the order in which the ideas in each group should be arranged by writing the number 1, 2, or 3 to the left of each sentence. If your arrangement is right, sentence 1 will present a topic and sentence 2 will present a supporting detail. Sentence 3 will then be a forceful restatement of the topic sentence.

A.

3. This is the aim of makers of quadraphonic systems.

1. Quadraphonic systems make records sound as much like the original performance as possible.

2. True quadraphonic reproduction adds nothing to the original sound and takes nothing from it.

1.

.... A meal can taste good but look bad.

.... A good meal appeals to all the senses.

.... The best meals please the eye and nose as well as the taste.

2.

.... Pets need to be watered and fed.

.... Keeping a pet is a responsibility.

.... A pet is more satisfying when it is properly cared for.

3.

.... People who plan ahead will have better vacations.

.... Planning a vacation takes imagination.

.... Plan something to do during your vacation.

EXERCISE B Decide whether the following groups of details should be arranged in *time order* or in *order of importance* (from least to most important). Then indicate the best order by writing the number 1, 2, or 3 in the space to the left of each sentence.

1.

.... Swing your right leg over the saddle of the bicycle.

.... Place your left foot on the left peddle of the bicycle.

.... Ride off on your bicycle.

2.

.... People vote for the Presidential ticket on the first Tuesday in November.

.... The major parties select their candidates for President and Vice-President in the summer preceding the election.

.... The President of the United States is inaugurated in January.

3.

.... The colonies achieved their independence from Great Britain.

.... The settlers gradually spread westward from the sea coast.

.... The first American colonists settled along the Atlantic coast.

4.

.... When she was young, Elizabeth Blackwell taught school.

.... Blackwell was the first woman to receive a medical degree in America.

.... Blackwell established the New York Infirmary for Women and Children.

WRITING PROJECT Choose one of the topics below (or one from Exercise A or B) and develop it into a paragraph. First make a list of details to include in your paragraph and decide whether they are best presented in time order or in order of importance. Be sure to keep out any details that do not help to develop your main idea, which should be stated in a topic sentence at some point in the paragraph.

PARAGRAPH TOPICS

1. How to water-ski, wash a car, plan a meal, organize a picnic, prepare a homework assignment, study for a test, or do anything else that requires practice or special skill
2. Losing and finding a pet
3. First impressions of a new neighbor
4. Eating a meal in a restaurant (at home or in the school cafeteria)
5. The worst day in the week (for you)

Effective Conclusions

The word *conclusion* has two separate meanings, but both apply to the kind of conclusion we are concerned with in a paragraph or theme. On the one hand, a conclusion is whatever comes at the end—for example, the last, or *concluding,* sentence of a paragraph. But a conclusion is also an idea that we arrive at through careful thinking, an idea that takes account of all the steps in our reasoning. The conclusion of a paragraph should pull together the ideas presented earlier and drive home to the readers the basic point that you want them to remember.

The concluding sentence of a paragraph sums up and restates the topic of the paragraph in the light of the details that have been presented.

The conclusion may simply say again, in a different and more forceful way, what has already been said in the topic sentence. More often, however, it will connect the topic with one or more of the important details presented in the paragraph. Notice the conclusion of the following paragraph.

TRAFFIC LIGHTS FOR SAFETY

At least two more traffic lights should be installed along East Main Street. The new Eastgate Shopping Center has attracted more traffic to that end of town than ever before, and traffic is especially heavy during the time when students are going to school. Since East Main passes just one block away from Harvey School, many students must cross despite the heavy traffic. We will have a serious accident some day unless the city makes it easier to cross East Main. *For the protection of Harvey students, traffic lights should be installed on East Main at both Ninth and Fifteenth Streets.*

The paragraph is developed by giving reasons that support the idea stated in the topic sentence—reasons for installing new traffic lights on East Main Street. Notice that the italicized conclusion repeats the topic sentence, but it adds two points not found at the beginning of the paragraph: (1) The conclusion adds the most important of all the reasons that have been given for the traffic lights ("for the protection of Harvey students"); and (2) it makes the main idea of the paragraph more definite—it suggests not just two traffic lights but traffic lights at two particular places, Ninth and Fifteenth Streets.

There are probably as many ways of rounding off a paragraph as there are paragraphs. Most paragraphs do, however, need a definite conclusion of some kind, and this is especially true of paragraphs that present information or try to persuade readers to accept the writer's ideas. Without a real concluding statement, the paragraph may simply trail off, leaving readers wondering what the point of it has been.

GOOD MANNERS

Good manners are a kind of social lubricant. Machinery requires lubrication to operate smoothly, and in the same way people who work together need good manners to help them get along. Good manners make difficult situations easier, especially when people who disagree or do not like each other must get along well whether they like it or not.

This paragraph is left hanging. It needs another sentence to act as a conclusion, to tell readers when the writer is through expressing opinions, and to remind readers what the point of the paragraph is.

When the topic sentence is placed at the end of the paragraph, it serves also as the conclusion of the paragraph.

THE BEST SEASONS OF THE YEAR

Some people like skiing and tobogganing and some people like swimming and camping out. I belong in this last group. For me, swimming and tennis and camping out are the best sports of all. As I see it, winter is just a time to get through as quickly as possible, so that I can begin my favorite activities again. *That's why, so far as I'm concerned, summer is the best season of the year.*

In a paragraph as short and simple as this one, there is really no need for separate topic and concluding sentences. With the topic sentence at the end, the paragraph has a definite, strong opening. It starts in at once with the writer's reasons for liking summer better than winter. Since most people are interested in sports, this makes an effective paragraph opening.

Do not introduce new material in the concluding sentence.

Notice how the last sentence weakens the effect of this paragraph.

WALKING IN THE RAIN

I love to walk in the rain. I can recommend it to anyone. Some people think I am crazy when I tell them this, but they don't know what they are missing. If you wear the right clothing, you can stay completely dry and comfortable, and see how different the world looks in the rain. *Walking in the country along back roads is also a delight.*

Disorganized conclusions are a sure mark of bad writing, for they cause a paragraph to lose its effectiveness. In this paragraph, after talking about walking in the rain, the writer has, in the last sentence, switched to a different topic. This leaves readers wondering what main idea the writer wanted to convey. Did the writer mean that walking in the rain is pleasant and that walking in the country, rain or shine, is pleasant also? Because the writer did not clearly conclude the main idea, the paragraph is not effective.

EXERCISE In the space provided after each paragraph, write a suitable concluding sentence. Try to make your concluding sentences restate the idea in the topic sentence in a more effective way. In some paragraphs, you should build into the conclusion the most important supporting detail in the paragraph. Be careful, however, not to introduce any completely new material in your concluding sentences.

1. Fine gardens take work. The most beautiful garden in our neighborhood belongs to Ms. O'Toole. She grows more different kinds of flowers than I have seen together anywhere except in parks. But she spends all her spare time working on her garden. As soon as she gets home from work, she goes out and works on her flowers. You could even say she was a slave to her garden.

Conclusion: . . . .

. . . .

2. Some people say they are afraid to fly in airplanes. They aren't afraid to take long trips in their cars, however. The truth is that many more people are injured in automobile accidents than in airplane crashes. Cars are much more dangerous than airplanes. No matter how careful drivers are, they can't protect themselves against the carelessness of strangers who may come speeding out of a side road at them.

Conclusion: . . . .

. . . .

3. It's hard to imagine today what our country looked like two hundred years ago. All of Indiana and Ohio were covered by forest, and in the great plains there were millions of acres of grass and gigantic herds of buffalo. Whole forests of huge pine trees which had taken centuries to grow were cut down in twenty or thirty years and can never be replaced.

Conclusion: . . . .

. . . .

4. Not many people realize how fast scientists have learned about the world we live in. Even though some basic discoveries were made long ago, most of our present scientific knowledge has been gathered during the twentieth century. It was only about a hundred years ago that doctors

learned about disease-causing germs, and modern methods of cancer research could not even be imagined fifty years ago.

Conclusion: ....

....

5. It's worthwhile to read magazines. No matter what you like to read, you can always find a magazine to suit you, and you'll probably be better off for reading it. Reading news magazines, for example, helps you to learn about other people and other places, and it is enjoyable as well. What's more, there are magazines for just about every hobby. You can find out new and interesting things about your hobby in hobby magazines and perhaps improve your skill.

Conclusion: ....

....

6. Some people talk too much. They just run off at the mouth, and I'm sure they don't know what they're saying. Sometimes I see two people walking along together, and they're *both* talking, right at the same time. Neither is really listening to the other. It's as if they were both making senseless noises, like monkeys in the zoo. What's the point of talking if it's nothing but noise? People ought to think over what they say before they say it, and then not talk unless the other person is interested and listening. Then what they say may count for something, and they wouldn't waste so much time and energy.

Conclusion: ....

....

WRITING PROJECT You should now be prepared to take a topic and build an effective paragraph on it, with a good opening, an effective development, and a strong conclusion. Keeping in mind all of the suggestions made so far in this chapter, choose one of the topics below and write a paragraph of several sentences on it. Remember that if the topic seems to you to be too broad, you must narrow it down to more workable size. If none of these topics interests you, pick one that does. It should be something with which you have had some experience, or of which you have acquired some knowledge.

PARAGRAPH TOPICS

1. One way for students to earn money
2. Getting acquainted in a completely new neighborhood
3. The thrill of long distance running
4. The advantages of a particular hobby
5. What causes people, once friends, to stop liking each other

© 1977 HBJ

Writing and Rewriting

Anything that you write represents *you* to your readers. Naturally, you want your compositions to be as good as you can make them—to represent you in the best possible light. That is why *re*writing a composition is often just as important as writing it in the first place.

When you put your ideas down on paper for the first time, don't worry too much about getting the composition letter-perfect all at once. Concentrate, instead, on finding the right words to express your ideas clearly and effectively. Then go over what you have written carefully, to be sure that your sentences and paragraphs say what you mean them to say and are free from usage blunders. Professional writers find that the best way of bringing a manuscript up to scratch is to read it several times, each time looking for a different kind of weakness or error.

Read a first draft for meaning.

When you write about something that you know very well, you may take mental shortcuts, assuming that your readers know as much about macramé or tie dyeing as you do. The chances are that they do not. As you reread your composition, ask yourself questions like these to be sure that your meaning is clear to your readers.

1. Is the main idea clearly stated in a topic sentence?
2. Are there enough details to develop the topic effectively?
3. Are the details presented in the most sensible order?

Read a first draft for sentence structure and variety.

Have you presented your ideas as well as you can? Ask yourself questions like these.

1. Is there enough variety in the sentences, or are they simply a string of childish simple sentences?
2. Are related ideas loosely strung together with *and*'s and *but*'s, or are phrases (prepositional phrases, appositives, *–ing* phrases) used to show the relationships of ideas precisely?
3. Is the choice of words precise and appropriate? Are there too many vague, general words or strings of modifiers that should be replaced with one good synonym?

Often, it is a good idea to leave usage and punctuation problems till the end, just before you make your final copy.

Read a first draft for errors in usage and mechanics (spelling, punctuation, capitalization).

In your final reading, keep a sharp eye for these points:

1. Does every sentence begin with a capital letter? Are other words correctly capitalized?

2. Have doubtful spellings been checked in a dictionary?

3. Does every verb agree with its subject? Are the correct pronoun forms in the right places?

4. Are there sentence errors to correct—fragments or run-ons?

5. Are any commas or other punctuation marks left out or misplaced? Are words in series, introductory word groups, and compound sentences correctly punctuated?

Let's see how these suggestions for revising your compositions might be put into practice. Here is a first draft of a short composition as a careless student might have written it.

1. We were very silly at camp. 2. One night. 3. Someone had a frog at our picknick, they put it in the dinning room under a stack of paper cups. 4. Dinner time come and someone picked up the cups. 5. The frog jump right into the potato sallad, no body wanted to eat any of that potato salid after that.

This paragraph is full of errors, as you can see, and it is also not very interesting. Yet it could, without too much rewriting, be made into quite a good theme. The writer is telling about something that really happened, trying to share a funny incident with readers.

Here are the things you would have to pay attention to if you were revising this paragraph to make it as good as it can be.

1. Meaning Sentence 1, the topic sentence, is not definite enough. It does not prepare readers for the amusing little incident that is coming. Notice also how vague the other sentences are—all about *someone, they* (sentence 3), and so on. We do not have a clear enough idea of the people in the incident to be interested in what happens. The incident is told in the right order, but it needs to be filled out with a few more details.

2. Sentence Variety Notice that every sentence except sentence 2 begins with the subject and verb. All of the sentences are about the same length. This lack of variety makes the paragraph boring for readers. Some of the sentences—sentence 3, for instance—could easily be varied by moving an adverb phrase to the beginning.

3. Errors in Usage and Mechanics Did you spot the three sentence errors? Sentence 2, a fragment, is really part of sentence 1. Sentences 3 and 5 are run-on sentences. There are also errors in spelling in sentences 3 and 5 and errors in verb usage in sentences 4 and 5.

238

Here is how the paragraph might be rewritten to eliminate all of these errors and weaknesses. Compare the sentences in the two versions of the paragraph. Try to find all the improvements in the rewritten paragraph.

IT HAPPENED AT CAMP

1. People sometimes do very silly things at camp. 2. One day, we were having a picnic lunch. 3. One of the girls found a frog at the lake. 4. She thought it would be a good idea to surprise people with it at dinner, and she hid it in the dining room under a stack of paper cups. 5. When dinner time came, someone picked up the cups. 6. Out leaped the frog, headfirst into a brimming bowl of potato salad. 7. Not a soul would eat any potato salad that night.

EXERCISE   On a separate sheet of paper, rewrite the following paragraphs, improving them as much as you can. Before you start your revision, read each paragraph several times. Think of additional details that you might use. Find ways of varying the sentences. Correct any errors in usage, mechanics, or spelling. Make whatever changes and additions you feel are needed, just as if you had written these first drafts yourself.

1. It is nice in the early morning. When every one is still asleep. The air smells fresh. On a nice day the sky is clear. You hear things that you wouldn't hear at other times. I like that time of day best.

2. One day when my parents were away from home I spent the whole day in the attic looking at old things. Such as magazines books furniture and an old trunk with old clothes and old dolls and boxes full of funny things my Mom and Dad save from a long time ago, I really enjoy looking around the attic like that.

3. Our beagle Sammy ran away from home last year. It was weeks before we found him. At least maybe he ran away or maybe he was kidnaped. I finally saw Sammy way over in the other part of town. Boy, was he ever glad to see us.

WRITING PROJECT   Write a paragraph on one of the topics below, or one of your own choosing. Plan to go over it thoroughly before you make your final copy, so that the version you hand in will be as good as you can make it.

1. Changing tastes (in cars, movies, or clothes)
2. Watching a professional football game (or any other sport)
3. My favorite jazz musician
4. Planning a party (scout meeting, picnic, etc.)
5. The best (or worst) day of my life
6. My favorite relative
7. Ten years from now (where will you be? what will you be doing?)
8. Learning to ride a horse (sail, ski, paint, etc.)
9. What I like about winter (or another season)
10. A personal hero (an astronaut? a hero of America's history?)

Writing Friendly Letters

If friends have been away for a while, there is always plenty to talk about when you next see them. You ask where they have been and what they have been doing, and they want to know about your activities, too. This is also the sort of thing that you write about in a friendly letter. A friendly letter takes the place of conversation.

In a friendly letter, write about things that interest you and the person to whom you are writing.

A letter is a special form of writing, in which you will put to work the writing skills that you have been practicing in this chapter. In particular, your letters should be put together in interesting, well-organized paragraphs that do not jump around from topic to topic. Avoid the vague "I am fine, how are you?" kind of letter. Fill out the paragraphs of a friendly letter with definite details, including information about things you have been doing that will be of interest. Ask your friends what they have been doing. Then your friends will enjoy your letter as much as Julie did Sheila's letter.

1743 Brian Avenue
Buffalo, New York 14221
September 30, 1976

Dear Julie,

School started almost a month ago now, but I still can't get used to the idea. It doesn't seem as real to me as camp. And to think that just six weeks ago we were all together enjoying ourselves at a beautiful lake! My mother says I spend too much time daydreaming, but, really, I'm just thinking about us at camp.

Do you remember the cove where we had the picnic that day when it began to rain? For some reason, that's the place I think about most. Next summer, it will be the first place I head for when I get back to camp.

I hope you can visit us during winter vacation. If there's enough snow, we can go skiing, and of course there will be ice-skating and tobogganing. Maybe we can even arrange a sleigh ride. But be prepared for cold weather. We have many days when the temperature stays close to zero, even at noon.

I was so excited when I got your letter that I ran upstairs to show it to Mother. Write me again as soon as you get a chance. And don't forget to make plans for New Year's in Buffalo.

With love,
Sheila

Follow generally accepted rules for the form of a friendly letter.

The rules for the form of a friendly letter are matters of common sense. They are meant to make your letter clear and neat and easier to read.

In general, your letters should be written on white, unruled paper. Write in blue or black ink—not pencil and not an odd shade of ink like red or green. (A typewritten letter is also acceptable, if you type well.) Center the whole letter on the page, with good margins all around. Follow the model letter below for letter form. Notice these points in particular.

1. Heading Write your address in two lines, with a comma between the city and the state. Leave a little space and then put your zip code number after the state. There should be no comma between the state and the zip code number. Write the date on the third line, with a comma between the day of the month and the year. Put no punctuation at the ends of these lines. The heading is usually written in *block style,* meaning that the three lines are lined up at the left.

2. Salutation Leave a little space between the heading and the salutation. Place the salutation at the left margin and put a comma after it.

3. Body Indent the first line of the letter and of each new paragraph. Other lines should line up evenly with the left margin.

4. Closing Capitalize the first word only. Begin the closing a little to the right of the center of the page. Put a comma after the closing. For someone whom you do not know very well, *Sincerely yours* is the most

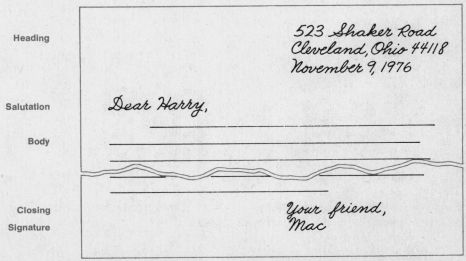

Heading	523 Shaker Road
	Cleveland, Ohio 44118
	November 9, 1976
Salutation	Dear Harry,
Body	
Closing	Your friend,
Signature	Mac

A Model for Friendly Letter Form

usual closing. Other closings, such as *Love* or *Your friend* are better for close friends.

5. Signature Line up your signature with the closing. If your name is short, it may be centered under the closing. It is best to sign your first and last name when you write to someone you do not know well.

6. Envelope Follow the model below. The return address (your name, street, city, state and zip code) should be in three lines at the upper left-hand corner. A comma is needed between the city and state. (Do not place a comma between the state and the zip code.) Center the address of the person to whom you are writing. Use a title (*Mr., Miss, Mrs., Ms., Dr.,* etc.) here but not in the return address. If it is not known whether a woman is married or single, you may choose to use *Ms.* as the title. Also use *Ms.* if it is known that this is the form of address the woman prefers.

Maxwell Shepherd
523 Shaker Road
Cleveland, Ohio 44118

Mr. Henry Duff
37 Locust Avenue
Lubbock, Texas 79404

A Model Envelope

WRITING PROJECT Write a friendly letter, with its envelope, to a friend of yours or a relative. Write neatly in ink on suitable paper, and follow the other rules of form given in this lesson. Organize your letter in well-constructed paragraphs and check it for errors before handing it in. The following questions may help you to think of interesting details to include.

1. What have you done recently that was unusual and that will interest your friend?
2. Have you read a book or seen a movie that you especially liked?
3. Have there been any odd or amusing incidents, at home or at school, that your friend would like to hear about?
4. Can you give news of other friends of yours that the person you are writing to also knows?

Writing Letters of Appreciation

A letter of appreciation is the special kind of friendly letter that we write when we wish to thank people for a kindness they have done us—for a present, an overnight visit in their home, or a particular favor of some kind. In form, a letter of appreciation is like any other friendly letter. The content of this kind of letter is determined by its purpose.

Follow these suggestions for the content of a letter of appreciation.

1. *Write promptly.* Delay in expressing your thanks for any kindness is discourteous. If someone has sent you a gift a prompt letter shows that the gift has been received and appreciated.

2. *Write enough.* A letter of appreciation need not be long, but it should be long enough to say what you like about the present or visit and to express a personal interest in the person to whom you are writing.

3. *Be sincere.* No one likes an exaggerated expression of thanks that the writer does not really mean. Often, the best way of expressing your appreciation is to tell the person you are thanking one or two definite things that you like about the gift or about your visit. Like all other writing, a good letter of appreciation is built from clear, definite details.

The following letters of appreciation show how the suggestions above can be applied. The first letter thanks someone for a gift. The second letter (page 244) thanks someone for a visit. After you have stayed for a few days in someone's home, it is a thoughtful gesture to write a personal letter of thanks to your hosts.

27 Lewis Drive
Ogden, Utah 84404
December 29, 1976

Dear Aunt Margaret,

How could you possibly have guessed that a new stamp album was one of the things I'd been hoping to get for Christmas? Dad's been saving the stamps from his foreign mail, and my collection has completely outgrown the old book. I've spent most of my time since Christmas reorganizing my stamps in the new album.

I hope your Christmas has been as pleasant as ours. It's been cold here since the beginning of vacation, and Lonnie and I have gotten in a lot of skating.

Again, thank you for your very thoughtful present.

Sincerely yours,
Waldo

367 River Street
Boston, Massachusetts 02106
August 17, 1976

Dear Mr. and Mrs. Stetson,

I had a wonderful time during my visit. The week in Philadelphia seemed to go by in a flash, with something new and interesting to do every moment. The day I spent at the newspaper office with you, Mrs. Stetson, was extremely interesting. I had never considered being a reporter before, but watching you work made the field seem so exciting that I now think it is what I want to do.

I also want to especially thank you, Mr. Stetson, for the tour of Temple University. I hadn't realized that it was quite so large. The library where you work particularly impressed me.

Mom and Dad tell me that they would be glad to have Marcia come and stay with us. They said they would get tickets to a play and perhaps we could go to the shore. We might even take a ride up to Salem, the site of the witch trials. They will be writing more about this to you soon.

Sincerely yours,
Debra Timons

WRITING PROJECT Write two letters of appreciation, one expressing thanks for a gift, the other for a visit to someone's home. If you wish, you may choose an imaginary situation like the ones listed below and write suitable letters, making up any additional details you may need. Follow the rules for the form of a friendly letter.

1. You have been given a hand-knitted sweater for a birthday present.
2. At Chanukah, you have been given a magic kit by an aunt and uncle whom you seldom see, because they live so far away.
3. You have been sick in bed, and some friends have sent you a book which you read with great interest.
4. You went to visit a friend in a big city, and they had something new and different planned for you every minute. For three days you were on the go constantly and scarcely had a chance to rest. But it was great fun.
5. You have spent a week with a friend whose family has a cabin in the mountains. While you were there, you went fishing in a lake with ice-cold water, you went climbing up mountains, and one morning you got up early to see the dawn on the mountainside.

Writing Business Letters

We often have occasion to write a business letter—to place an order, perhaps, or to request help or information from some organization. Use the business letter below as a model for your own business letters.

Follow generally accepted rules for the form of a business letter.

1. Heading Write your complete address and the date in three lines. The only commas needed are those between the city and state (with its zip code), and between the day of the month and the year.

2. Inside Address Put the inside address at the left margin. It should include the complete name and address of the person or organization (or both) that you are writing to.

3. Salutation Notice that in a business letter the salutation is followed by a colon, not a comma. Your letter may be addressed to an individual within a company when the name is known (Dear Mr. Hudson, Dear Ms. Prinz). Otherwise, address the letter by title only (Dear Sales Manager, Dear Director). If you are writing to a company in general, the traditional salutation is *Gentlemen* or *Dear Sir*. It is understood, of course, that the

Heading	41 Ryan Road Augusta, Georgia 30904 February 4, 1976
Inside Address	Durham Crafts Company 33 Lambeth Circle Durham, North Carolina 27705
Salutation	Gentlemen:
Body	Please send me, by parcel post, the following items as listed in your latest catalogue: 1 leather tooling set $2.25 12 lacing needles 1.50 $3.75 I am enclosing a money order for $3.75, plus 50¢ to cover postage, a total of $4.25.
Closing **Signature**	Yours truly, *Harold Mason* Harold Mason

A Model Business Letter

group you are writing to may be composed of both men and women. Leave space between the inside address and the salutation.

4. Body Leave extra space between the salutation and the body of the letter. Notice the indentation for the first line and each new paragraph (5 spaces in a typewritten letter).

5. Closing Leave space below the body of the letter and begin the closing a little to the right of the center of the page. *Yours truly* or *Very truly yours* (followed by a comma) is the usual closing for a business letter. Only the first word is capitalized.

6. Signature Write your name clearly. In a typewritten letter, the signature is typed below the written signature.

As you should have noticed, the *form* of a business letter differs from that of a friendly letter in a number of ways. These differences in form reflect differences in content that are even more important.

Follow these suggestions when you write a business letter.

1. *Be brief.* A business firm that does its business through the mail may receive thousands of letters and orders every day. If you clutter up your business letters with unnecessary details or personal comments, your request may be delayed or handled incorrectly.

2. *Be clear and complete.* Give all the necessary information and arrange it (as in the order letter on page 245) so that it will be easy to follow. Be definite about what you want and whether you are placing an order or merely asking for information.

3. *Be neat.* If your letter is smudgy or messy, full of erasures and crossed out words, it may not receive the kind of attention you want. Typing is preferred for a business letter, if you type well. This also makes it easy to keep a carbon copy of your letter. (On a carbon copy, the inside address provides a record of the person or organization to whom you wrote.) If your letter is handwritten, it should be in ink, and you should keep a copy or a summary for later reference. Use plain white paper only, preferably $8\frac{1}{2}$ x 11-inch typing paper, whether the letter is typed or handwritten.

Notice how the letter on page 247, a request for information, carries out the various suggestions for business letters that have been made in this lesson.

WRITING PROJECT Choose one of the letter ideas in each group and write the appropriate business letter. Type the letters or write them in ink, following the suggestions in the lesson. Prepare an envelope for each letter.

246

1. Write to a book publisher asking for a catalogue of books on any subject that interests you.
2. Write to the director of a summer camp asking for information about camp next summer. Ask for definite information, such as dates, costs, transportation to the camp, activities, special equipment needed, and so on.

ORDER LETTERS

1. From a newspaper or magazine cut out an advertisement for something that you would like to order by mail. Write the letter ordering the merchandise, saying how you will pay for it (money order, C.O.D., etc.) and how you would like it sent. Attach the advertisement to your letter when you hand it in.
2. You have seen an advertisement for a six-foot surplus toboggan, at a price of $24.95 postpaid. Order this from Gateway Service Supply, 1927 Jennings Lane, Evansville, Indiana 47712. Indicate that you are enclosing payment.

```
                                    2802 Heather Place
                                    Boise, Idaho 83702
                                    January 25, 1976

The American Library Association
50 East Huron Street
Chicago, Illinois 60611

Gentlemen:

     Our seventh-grade English class is planning a
classroom display for National Library Week.  We
understand that you can furnish posters, book lists,
and other materials for use during National Library
Week, both for bulletin boards and for distribution
to students and parents.

     Please send me a list of the materials avail-
able, indicating the cost of any items for which
there is a charge.

                                    Very truly yours,

                                    Linda Bowman
                                    Linda Bowman
```

A Model Request for Information

INDEX

INDEX OF VOCABULARY WORDS
(Page numbers refer to definition in text)

A NOTE ON SPELLING

Writing may be thought of as a way of recording the sounds of speech by the use of symbols that represent those sounds. The letters in our alphabet are the symbols we use to represent our speech sounds. If we had a different letter for each sound, spelling would be easy; just a matter of knowing which letter to use for each sound. Unfortunately, English spelling is not that simple. There are more sounds than there are letters in the alphabet to represent them, and so the task of learning to spell in our language is somewhat complicated.

The complications, however, may be partially overcome by becoming aware of, and learning, the many *spelling patterns* that do exist. These patterns involve the use of various combinations of letters to spell certain sounds.

To show the *sounds* of a word, rather than the letters, a special phonetic alphabet has been developed. Using this phonetic alphabet will help you understand the relationship between sounds and letters, and thereby help you to become a better speller.

On the next page and the inside back cover are two charts. The first one, entitled "Consonant Sounds and Their Common Spellings," summarizes twenty-four main consonant sounds of English, the symbols used to represent these sounds, and common ways of spelling them. The *symbol* for each consonant sound is written between a pair of slanted lines. For example, the symbol /k/ stands for the sound of the first letter in the word *kit*, as you can see by looking at the chart. The sound /k/ may also be spelled by the letters *c* (as in *cold*), *ck* (as in *lick*), or *ke* (as in *like*).

The second chart, "Vowel Sounds and Their Common Spellings," shows the symbols for fourteen main vowel sounds, and the vowel sound called a *schwa*. If you look at the vowel sound /ī/ on the chart, you will see the several patterns or ways in which this sound may be spelled. For example, in the word *line*, it is spelled with the letter *i* followed by a consonant (*n*), which, in turn, is followed by an *e*. (The letters **VCe**, standing for *vowel, consonant, e,* represent *one* of the ways or patterns in which the sound /ī/ may be written in English.) Other ways include *–igh* as in *high; –y* as in *try; –ie* as in *die*.

The spelling patterns reflected in these two charts should help to balance the irregularities of English spelling. The point is, that *despite* exceptions and seemingly illogical spellings, our spelling system exists as it does for good historical reasons, and is, on the whole, a predictable system.

Consonant Sounds and Their Common Spellings

Sound	At the Beginning	At the End
/p/	**p:** pie	**p:** rip; **pe:** ripe
/t/	**t:** ten	**t:** pet; **te:** date
/k/	**k:** kit; **c:** cold	**ck:** lick; **ke:** like
/ch/	**ch:** chin	**tch:** witch; **ch:** reach
/b/	**b:** bed	**b:** tub; **be:** tube
/d/	**d:** do	**d:** rid; **de:** ride
/g/	**g:** get	**g:** beg; **gue:** league
/j/	**j:** jet; **g:** gentle	**dge:** budge; **ge:** cage
/f/	**f:** fun; **ph:** phrase	**ff:** stuff; **fe:** life; **f:** beef; **ph:** paragraph
/v/	**v:** very	**ve:** save
/s/	**s:** see; **c:** center	**ss:** glass; **s:** bus; **se:** case; **ce:** rice
/z/	**z:** zoo	**z:** quiz; **zz:** buzz; **se:** rose; **ze:** sneeze
/sh/	**sh:** ship	**sh:** push
/zh/	**j:** Jacques	**ge:** rouge; (in the middle) **s:** treasure
/r/	**r:** run; **wr:** wrist; **rh:** rhyme	**r:** car; **re:** care
/l/	**l:** lose	**ll:** pill; **le:** smile; **l:** fail
/m/	**m:** move	**m:** Sam; **me:** same; **mb:** tomb
/n/	**n:** nose; **gn:** gnaw; **kn:** know	**n:** pin; **ne:** pine
/ng/		**ng:** strong; **n:** trunk
/th/	**th:** thick	**th:** path
/th/	**th:** then	**th:** smooth; **the:** bathe
/y/	**y:** you; **u** /y-ū/: use	
/w/	**w:** will; **o** /w-u/: one; **qu** /k-w/: quick	
/h/	**h:** hat; **wh:** who	